Chapter 1

As the old Greek said, anything worth the telling has a beginning, a middle and an end. I must tell you the whole story, good and bad. To begin at the beginning .... my name is Terry and I was born in Toronto on the 6th of June, 1960. My two brothers and two sisters came later, and were all born in the hospital, like other children. But I came into the world at home in number 7, Sudbury Street, in Parkdale; I always wondered why I was the only one born in a house?.

Toronto is the most modern of cities, laid out like a brand-new, shining checker-board. Not even the mounds of dirty snow in March can tarnish the gloss. No slums, no eyesores in our town; it somehow always reminded me of a dentist's clinic stacked with row upon row of shiny false teeth, or a dresser of delph. My hometown, lovely though it is, left me numb; everything left me stone-cold back then. From the word go I had as much feeling in me as a fish. There was something rotten in the state of Denmark; I just didn't fit in. Only for the face, I could have been an Indian papoose lost in this white man's land, searching for vanished footprints, sadly listening to the singing, lingering place-names, not a wigwam in sight. Where on earth had I turned up from?

We Torontonians sure are proud of our modern streets and our silent subway running like clockwork. Bloor running east west and Yonge north south is said to be the biggest cross-roads in the world. On Sudbury Street we had Lake Ontario out in front, in all her moods from ice to dappling sunshine. We children had the park to play in just around the corner. Niagara Falls was only a picnic away. Toronto, on Uncle Sam's back-doorstep, the mecca of every tribe under the sun, Toronto, city of tongues. the new Babylon. They used to say then, back in the sixties, that nobody over ten in our street was born in Canada. Blow-ins one and all, and the latest nomads kept on coming from the four winds; we could spot them a mile away in the clothes they stood up in. Whatever the question, whatever the language, the answer was always the same, "Ask in Foley's pub". That was three doors down from us. In this world of aliens, I was the oddest alien of them all.

I was baptised in Holy Family parish on King Street. But it was in St. Patrick's on Dundas Street that I made my First Communion. That's all Chinatown today; it was Irishtown then, an Irish stew with a peppering of Chinese, Malayans, Hawaiians, Filipinos, to give it a bit of an oriental flavour.

In our own little melting-pot at number seven, we were indeed a mixed breed, in more ways than one. For a start we were what the Spaniards politely call mestizos and mulattos. My father came from the island of Samar in the south-eastern Philippines. His name was Raul Cruz; he was an Aglipayan, a splinter religion that had broken off from Rome at the time of the revolution against Spain. My mother was Irish. Her name was Maggy Atwell, and she came from an island in Upper Lough Erne in County Fermanagh. She had a Protestant father and a Catholic mother by the name of Maguire. A mongrel bunch we were indeed, even for Toronto. Sudbury Street was mainly a Catholic Filipino-Irish bailiwick then, a mecca for migrants from two corners of the earth as far apart as they could come, yet birds of a feather. The cross-breeding showed visibly only in me; one brother and one sister are oriental in appearance, could pass for full Filipinos; the other brother and sister are as Irish as Paddy's pig. I'm neither fish nor flesh, a Chinese-Malayan with slanty green eyes and red hair and a button nose. I stuck out like a sore thumb from the word go. Even in Sudbury street I was an oddity. I drew the quizzical stare, the raisd eyebrow, the double-take, the snide, half-heard snigger. I was a freak. Blushing like a lobster to the roots of my carrot hair only made it worse. For as long as I can remember I felt ashamed, wanting to run and hide, as a poor, frightened, shy wild animal in the zoo must surely feel naked in it's cage, exposed to the vulgar stares of the gawking humans.

All through the middle sixties when I was growing up, ours was a kind of half-way house for the travellers. Transients came and went at all hours. It was a home-from-home for aliens, legal and otherwise. Various cousins and neighbours constantly came and went by land and sea and then by air. They staggered in from the pub. They stayed a night, a week, a month, till they found work. No.7, Sudbury street, Parkdale, Toronto, Canada, they knew that address by heart in potato-fields and rice-paddies, in dancehalls and pubs. For sailors working their passage, it was often the only English they knew. They came in swarms, like bees to honey, like Muslims to Mecca. Ours was the famous open door, a place to stay, a shakedown, always something to eat, fiesta all year round, that was our house, an Irish Filipino hodge-podge of talking and singing in a babble of dialects and accents. Maggy ran an oasis for the nomads, an asylum for the jobless, even down to cock-fights and pitch-and-toss in the back yard. I'll say this much for Maggy, she never forgot the open arms that welcomed her and took her in, when she herself, as a young girl, flew the coop, to face the vast, terrifying white city of strangers. She was a big woman with a big heart. She was a soft touch. There were always exceptions to prove the rule, but mostly the women were grateful to her and did not forget; among the men she put up with more than her fair share of spongers and dossers, who never so much as said thanks.

Very early on I learned my lesson, this is a man's world. Midnight or high-noon, guitars might be strumming, men arguing politics, yarns spinning in a babel of tongues. The crack was rich, if you happened to be a man. What wit and humour. The Paddies and the Phils got on great, and they got most of their mileage out of slagging the women; no end of jokes about the oul lassy (that could be the wife, the mother, the girl-friend, or the mother-in-law). Boys will be boys, but the squaws were fair game and were vetted into lots, like cattle or tires, brand new,

3

second hand, hitched, bespoke. recycled. Phil suited the action to the word and made hay. But Paddy, behide the guff, was a craven puritan oozing guilt and hot air; he'd far rather nurse a pint in his fist than a doxy on his knee. Short of hell-hire, he dreaded getting hooked with a bun in the oven. The Orangeman got his dig in, "Your weemen have yez be the short hairs; they run to the priest in the box".

I have never ceased to marvel that the Irish and the Filipinos, of whatever persuasion or none, from the two ends of the earth, had so much in common, the music, the humour, the close family bonds, the suffocating family ties, the fierce family feuds, the smothered loves and cherished hates, the whole macho myth. It was a man's world; didn't the Bible say so; only men counted. On the other hand, behind all the swagger and bravado, the machismo and bragging, was the contradiction, and I sensed it very early on; men were only spoiled brats, little boys who never grew up. It was the women who really ran the show and ruled the roost, and played along with the make-believe, because that's the way they wanted it; they thought that was the only way they could survive. Talk about a tangled net, a vicious circle; this was what I was brought up on. In their heart of hearts the women well knew that the men were still little boys whose mothers never let them grow up, and they proceeded to do the same with their own sons. The webs we weave. Children dont miss much; you learned early in 7 Sudbury. Of course I'm looking back now with the benefit of hindsight at my childhood, but I'm not merely reading back by any means. Only too well do I remember the way it was. At four I was a very confused rebel, mad at the world, afraid, lonely, jealous, miserable. I had guilt too; it was my fault somehow. And a fierce curiosity to find out why, why, why?

At the same time, in my heart of hearts I knew something else; God loves me. God is love. That is who he is. I always knew that. He told me so Himself. His only law is love. Every child knows it, craves it. But men and women are always hurting one another. In the catechism class at school, the teacher told us that

4

we were all infected with original sin, because Adam and Eve ate the apple. I thought that was pretty silly. The way I saw it, all sin is rank selfishness, not loving enough; we say we love one another and still we hurt one another. Parents pass on the bad as well as the good to their children, and so it goes, on and on. That was original sin for me. It should be called the sins of the fathers and the mothers. We inherit both the good and bad in our genes. I was the living proof. You see, no one told me I was an ill-bred brat, a get; I just knew in the pit of my stomach from as long as I can remember that I was, in very truth, a bastard, God bless the mark.

It was from Raul, of all people, that I picked up this idea, very early on, about the mammas and the pappas; he had chunks of the bible off by heart from his own Aglipayan childhood, and as Shakespeare says about the devil, Raul was a past master at quoting scripture when it suited his purpose. A favourite with him was, "The fathers eat sour grapes and the children's teeth are set on edge; what about the sins of the so-and-so mothers?". What goes on in the mind of a child when mammy and daddy have a row? Who of us can remember how that was at five? When the storm blew over, wasn't there making-up time? Weren't there hugs and kisses in your house, and didn't you crawl into the warm nest? Who can imagine the heart of a child who lives in the eye of the storm, and was never fondled even once? In it's awful loneliness, forever on the outside looking in at the goodies, it whispers, "My mammy and daddy are not my real mammy and daddy at all. I have no one of my own in the whole wide world. Where? who? why, why, why?" That was me, confused, alone, angry, afraid, a poor homing pidgeon lost in the storm, dreaming a hopeless dream of finding that warm body. Our house was a hive, but my pillow was often wet. Then I couldn't even cry, my heart as cold as a stone. At seven I set out to prepare for first communion and to find her. I craved a warm lap to nestle in, a smiling face to talk to, a mother to love me. Even now I cant put it into words, that hankering for the touch of a vanished hand. A bastard wakens up quick to the facts of life, and nurses a mini volcano, all bottled up inside.

The others wouldn't play with me; I never had a doll. My game was wondering who was the spoiled brat bully-boy who had to have everything he laid his eyes on or he would kill it. Then he walked away. Who was the girl? Which of them had the green eyes? Did she walk away too? Where is she now? People count sheep when they cant sleep at night; I used to line up words, amor, love, gradh, gugma, mama. What language did she speak? Was she the Irish in me or the Filipina? It was like picking at a sore. Before I could think, or put it in words, I had this fierce drive in me, to find her, alive or dead, if it took me the rest of my life. This I lived for. I had no childhood, only this fierce drive in my one-track mind.

Maggy ran a tight ship. The cops looked in from time to time and shared what was going. They knew the score and asked no questions about aliens, legal or otherwise; except for Indians and Eskimos, weren't they all blow-ins and wet-backs and narrow-backs. The Phils cant drink; the Paddies cant stop, and soaked up enough booze for both. Anyone who couldn't sleep it off quietly was out on his ear. For ten years Maggy and Raul had no children. She was a stout woman; beside her he was a featherweight, a banty-cock. Finally I arrived, then four more in quick succession. Looking back now, I couldn't have got a better education; I could curse fluently in six languages as soon as I could talk. It was a colourful childhood, never a dull waking moment. It was terrible too; I was a nobody with no arms to hug me and tell me I was wanted. Mama is the same in any language; I called her in the dark; she never came. Nobody wanted Terry.

We youngsters would often drop off from sheer exhaustion in the middle of the bedlam, and sleep right through it all. Someone, a distant aunt or a cousin by the button-hole, might carry or sleep-walk me upstairs to the attic. Where was Raul? Children dont miss much; I twigged it very early. He wasn't wasting his time arguing politics in the sala, telling the same old crude jokes that belittle women; he had better things to do with his time. The Phils and the Irish agreed on the basics of life; of course it was a man's world. For God's sake, wasn't Eve only an

6

afterthought, cobbled out of Adam's spare rib. They merely differed as to taste; Paddy liked his poison out of a bottle; the geni with the lovely frothy head on her was his baby and bedfellow. Phil preferred what is known in polite circles as cleaning his gun on a regular basis, ha, ha, ha! Raul owed it to his manhood. Wading up to his knees in mud behind his carabao in the rice-paddy back home, with only a rag covering his quan, a man can barely afford one woman; but a carida on the side shows you're going up in the world. She was always Raul's niece, maryah; this was Canada after all and one had to observe the niceties. Raul was not one for drunken talk; he was a man of action. Pick your poison. The Phils hoored and the Paddies pissed agen the wall.

The long-suffering Maggy had a big heart but a weak head. Her days were spent working two jobs in the hospital, cooking for the wayfarers, drinking innumerable mugs of tea you could trot a mouse on, and talking gossip. Wee Raul, with a couple of drinks gone to his head, would swagger back from his nightly pilgrimage and take into big Maggy, just to show the man he was. He'd work himself up into a froth and the next thing, he was blubbering, all awash in self-pity; from abusing Maggy one minute he'd start cursing his own mother the next. I'd be listening, trying to make sense of his mad raving about his Aglipayan childhood; he seemed riddled with guilt but blamed his mother for spoiling him rotten. After all, it was the damn women's own so-and-so fault; didn't the mothers rule the roost and lay down the law in the first place? They sowed the wind and everybody reaped the whirlwind. I could see it. His mother had him running around in a shift that barely covered his navel till he was ten. She stroked his head while he stroked his gamecock and watched his poor sisters slaving away, doing all the work. She cuddled her vicious little monster in her lap and all the girls got was the back of her hand. He'd take a sudden vicious swipe at Maggy and she'd smother him in her mighty arms and pacify him and half-carry him off to bed and tuck him in like a baby. Talk about being spoiled. In two minutes flat he'd be snoring. She should have knocked him into the middle of next week, the first time he tried to lay a hand on her. That might have made a real man of him. Instead he'd end up in her lap. She fell for it every time.

My brothers and sisters would worm into the huddle and they'd all hug and enjoy a good cry for themselves, often to the tune of a boozy, rebel war-chant about Mother Ireland, or the Sash me father wore, or a doleful Filipino ditty of blighted love, from the bachelor chorus. And I was left out in the cold. I didn't belong. They could all fight and make up; but they could do no wrong. To rub salt in the wound they all seemed to take it out on me. I was the outsider; I was the odd-ball. Turkeys will fight among themselves, then gang up on the odd one; I was always different, on the outside looking in. I cant remember now the first time it hit that I didn't belong to them at all; I had to be adopted. From the very start I was looking for someone to love me; I ached for arms around me. In our house there was never a dull moment, but I was all alone. Looking back now, I am still that lost soul, struggling to put the heart-ache into words.

Maggy got a better chance than most Irish and Filipino women of past generations. Her own father treated her mother like a queen. He let her have her way; he made no bones about her raising all the children Catholics. It was grossly unfair; the arrogance of Rome, but he let it be. Every Sunday he brought her and the children to Mass in the cot, and then marched off by himself to the Presbyterian church. Maggy took St. Paul's words, "Wives, be submissive to your husbands", too literally, and took refuge in good works and gossip and strong tea. These things must be handed down. I soon saw that Irish mothers spoil their sons rotten too. A dog will become a tyrant if you make yourself his slave. I used to wonder why mothers did it, till it dawned on me that it's a control thing; the slave can manage the tyrant if she plays her cards right. When the spoiled brat who never got the chance to grow up, finally escapes from the apron-strings, some other poor woman and her children have to take the brunt of it. Woman's apron-strings are elastic; the son

8

never escapes entirely; ma hugs her slavery and holds onto her darling son and keeps herself and everyone else miserable, and so it goes, on and on. A pampered gamecock in his blind fury will kill, kill, kill, even attacking the hens that wont crouch in terror and submit to his savage rape. Man is the worst killer on the planet. But who put every mother's son up to it? A tangled web only God's magic can unravel.

Thinking back now, this was heavy, ugly stuff for a child to be grappling with; I learned the facts of life early. I still have it stuck in my craw; it burns me up. In the fierce arguments in our house the Orangeman would slag, "The weemen run to the hole in the wall and spill the beans to the priests; them's the boys keeps yez all under their thumb". So it goes on and on, down the generations. It's how we try to cope, to survive; controlling someone or something, if it's only a pet cat. It's the name of the game. In my child's mind I too tried to cope, as I came slowly and painfully through the mill. The Bible says the sins of the fathers are visited on the children; what about the sins of the mothers? What did I know? What do I know now? What does anybody know about what goes on in other people's heads? But when you're only five or six and lonely as bedamned with no one to talk to, listening to the grown-up talk, you wonder about many things. People are selfish. That's original sin; somehow I'm the rotten fruit of it, left to live by my wits.

I expected nothing from Raul for I knew he hadn't it in him to love anyone only himself. In a way he couldn't help it. But Maggy baffled me. She had an open heart for every go-the-road that darkened the door; she was good to me in many ways; I never went hungry. Yet she never touched me, as if I had leprosy; what had she against me? I was an angry and confused child as well as a lonely one. I remember well how I felt the first time I heard about the untouchables in India. I said to myself, "At least they have fathers and mothers who touch them". In my very bones I felt like an alien from Mars.

But at long last the worm turned, Maggy I mean, not me. The Presbyterian grit buried deep somewhere inside her, finally came to the surface. One night Raul came home from target practice early in a foul mood, to find a hooley in full swing, and a bevy of women in the kitchen. Had he lost money on the nags? Maybe his current dalaga was not available that night to console him. Whatever the reason, he was in a vicious temper. Had someone slipped a double shot of something in the Ma's tay unbeknownst, for the crack? She never touched the stuff. Anyway this time, instead of turning the other cheek as usual, she now smiled sweetly down at him and remarked to her girl friends, "Hasn't Raul the cutest wee nose, as bright as a button?". That blew it. Men have killed for less. No greater insult can be levelled at a red-blooded Filipino; it's a direct attack on his manhood, a verbal kick in the crotch. All over the East, the nose is an infallible clue to the dimensions of that other precious vital organ. She was politely calling him a bayute, which can be anything from a pansy to a full-blown homo. One can admire the female nose and it's taken as a compliment. But the male proboscis is a sore spot, the target of infinite jest with the women among themselves. Wee Raul saw red. He came at her like a wet bantycock. But this time, instead of hush-hushing him and smoothing his ruffled feathers, she hauled back her brawny arm and clobbered him smack on his wee pug nose, and sat him neatly on his arse in the middle of the kitchen floor. Exit Raul never to be seen again while she lived. He had lost face and marbles, a fate worse than death.

Maggy was better off without him, only she didn't know it. She was now riddled with guilt. And, for some strange reason which I could never fathom, it was all my fault that he was gone and that she was miserable. She took it out on me. In our house the crack was rich and I laughed a lot, but only to keep from crying. There was that hollow inside that nothing could fill, and I had nobody I could talk to about it. Laughing and fun, lonesomeness and longing, forever getting picked on right or wrong, that is the childhood I remember. But I'm getting away ahead of myself.

A vivid memory from very early on is with me still. Perhaps I was no more than three or four at the time. The whole scene, with all the colours and sounds, the feel, and even the smell of it, is still vivid as I write. I wakened half-frozen in the freezing black of the Canada winter to the hubbub from below. Groping my way down the stairs in the dark, my bleary eyes could just make out a figure huddled on the bottom step, a little man gently strumming a guitar and crooning mournfully to himself, "Gugma ko, ngano ba intawon naglimbong ka? - My love, whyever did you forsake me?". A gamecock nestled in his lap. It reminds me now of a ventriloquist and his dummy. Each time the man paused to draw breath in this doleful ditty, the cock stretched his neck and sang, "Cock-a-doodle-do". A drunken debate still raged in the sala, a jumble of names, Pearse and Paisley, Imelda and Magsaysay, Dev and Tone, Hucs and Orangemen, wafting out on a wave of stale porter and roasted coffee. From the front parlour came the drone of a Latin Mass, Dominus vobiscum. Maybe it was that morning I first got the hankering to find - what? The wee man with his sad song and his gamecock, the old greyhaired priest with his mumbling Latin, Imelda and her mountain of shoes, all the love and the hate, all the heart-ache, why, why, why? No doubt I'm reading back from where I now stand, but right or wrong, we have only our memories to tell us how it once was. I'm still struggling to put in words what I could then only feel in my vitals. I had a pain like an empty hole inside; that I know. The worst part of it all was that no one, not even Maggy, with all her kindness to every down-and-out, had ever touched me, and I couldn't talk to a soul. I was dumb.

Even now, I still cant put that awful time in words. The crack was rich; we laughed a lot. But I went to my cold bed alone, with an empty hole in the pit of my stomach. That time still haunts my dreams and I am that poor little mite again, and wake up crying for my mama, but no sound comes out and no one answers. All I ever wanted was to be wanted, arms to hold me and a voice to whisper in my ear, "Hush a bye baby, I love you".

Chapter 2

Over the years I kept these feelings locked up inside, with no one to talk to, only God. He was both father and mother to me; He never went away or my heart would have died. The Filipinos have a telling expression, gawas sa mosquitero, outside the mosquito-net. Perhaps it was the braggart stories I was weaned on instead of mother's milk, about men's cruel, pitiful conquests over wretched, so-called easy women, that first put the wild idea in my head that I was not the child of Raul and Maggy at all, that I was a love-child without love. Of course I'm looking back now with the benefit of hindsight. The hankering grew into a hunger, a craving, an obsession with me. All I ever wanted was her arms around me, her words whispering, "Hush, little one, Mama's here". Had she ever touched me? Had I suckled her breasts even once?

To find her became my whole life, my all. Later on I learned that I was searching for myself as well, my own lost identity, to get to know where my mixture of Irish and Filipino blood had come from, in order to find out where I had come from, to find me. I had to know. I never breathed a word to a living soul; how could I? and anyway, who cared? By the time I reached high-school I had it all worked out; my sights were set. This was my secret, my goal in life. No lover-boys for me. I had to find my mother, if it took me the rest of my life. Maggy surely had to know who my real mother was, if not who my father was too, but how could I ask her? Indeed, she was the last person I would dare ask. In my heart I knew I wasn't hers, but how can you ask your mother who your real mother was? I was always on my own.

Then the miracle happened. When I was six a break came in the clouds, though the hurt never went away. From then on the holidays was the magic time. I was lucky to have not one but two grannies, so it was off to Gran Ketty in Ireland in summer, and to Tia Maria in the Philippines for Christmas. I never thought of asking where this miracle came from; I suppose I just took it for granted that they were all glad to get rid of me for awhile. There was always some kindly, motherly soul in transit, to take me under her wing and see me both ways safely.

Lazy oldfashioned Ireland was some change from spic-and-span Toronto, our shiny clockwork city, with it's bone-chilling cold for months on end, then suddenly the blast-furnace heat for the rest of the year. What a magic place the country is to a towny. The first time the plane came in over the Cliffs of Moher and I saw this lovely picture; it took my breath away, the pure, fresh greenness of it, the colours, the endless variety. Every time since, the coolness comes as a fresh shock. And it was always changing, every few minutes; one minute it was raining, the next the sun was out again, like crying and laughing together twenty times a day. Above all else it was the sounds that meant Ireland to me, music, people talking, birds singing, water-fowl calling, hens cackling and scolding in the morning. That first time I went with Molly, a neighbour of Maggy's back home. I slept in her lap on the plane. Ireland was many things to me as a child, a corncrake rasping away in the dark, the smell of turf-smoke, the big, heavy copper penny with the hen and chickens on it, that got me my first stick of Peggy's Leg.

Gran Ketty lived on an island called Goladuff in Upper Lough Erne. What a contrast that was to the life I was used to. As I said, we are proud of our beautiful white city, so modern and tidy, the acres of concrete, the silent subway running on the dot, the neon lights, the ice-hockey, the baseball, the street-cars, the hurrying throngs. And we have our mighty Lake Ontario, our very own inland sea, and the beautiful island, and the wideopen spaces of High Park. Beautiful Toronto, but even as a child I could see it was mostly manmade. God made Lough Erne and it is still the way it was the day it left His hand. I fell asleep on the long bus journey. Molly woke me, "That's Lough Erne shining through the trees; we're nearly there". A man was waiting at a stone bridge,"That's your Uncle Robby". We tied my little suitcase to the carrier of Uncle Robby's bicycle as Molly waved so-long from the bus window. It was two miles on the bar of the bicycle, then three fields on foot to the lough shore. Uncle Robby said nothing until we got there. "Be damn but the cot's gone", says he and threw back his head and cheered. Mournful howls answered over the low hills, "Them bloody tongue-hounds", Uncle Robby muttered and I hadn't a clue. We sat on the turf in a shed out of a sudden shower and the sun came out again and made a little rainbow on the water. Uncle Robby hadn't much to say except, "It's about time", and a man in a low black boat came over the water out of the fading rainbow. And so we crossed over to Goladuff.

Gran Ketty always made much of me; hers was my first real hug. She had no electric light in her house, only a tilley lamp. There was no toilet; you had to go out in the haggard when no one was about. I had so much to learn. No clockwork here; everything took it's own sweet time. I plagued Gran with questions, "what's that"? We wandered about the livelong day and she taught me the names of all the sights and sounds. The crickets would be chirping in the chimley, and the kettle would be gurgling on the hob, and the hens arguing and scolding on the street from dawn to dark. When it rained they ran for shelter looking draggled and miserable, and the ducks splashed and laughed and jeered at the droopy-drawers hens. I soaked it all up like a sponge. I soon knew the clear piping song of the blackbird and the linnet and all the finches, and the lark singing up the sky at heaven's door, and the full notes of the thrush repeating herself. Out on the lough the baldies and waterhens and wild-duck and snipe and curlew and lapwings went on calling all through the night, and I lay awake to listen.

People came for a cayley in the evening; I'd hear the rattle of an oar and the water plashing against a cot-side; then the low voices would come drifting up slowly towards the house. They sat around the fire and talked about the state of the world and told yarns and drank big mugs of tea. I drank it all in. Some had crazy stories like the one about the ass and the sow; 'Jem's wife died and he married Biddy. When Biddy moved in with him she let her own wee house to a lodger named Tom, whose chief

14

occupation in life was drinking. One church holiday she ordered Jem to go round after Mass and check and see how things were faring with the lodger. Tom was away on business but the door was on the latch. Jem went in to have a look around. There was a hole in the mud wall between the kitchen and the lower room. Jem peered in through the hole. "Aha", says he, "a wheelrake. How in hell did he get the wheelrake in there?". He looked again; his eyes were getting used to the dim light; he saw that it was not a wheelrake at all but the ribs of a dead ass. It took Jem a while but he finally figured out what had happened; Tom slept in the upper room and had the ass lodging in the lower room and the sow had the kitchen to herself. They were all nice and comfortable until the ass died. The sow burrowed through the mud wall when she got Tom away and ate the ass". They would chuckle and click their tongues in wonder, 'Boys o' boys'.

The talk was often serious as well. The house was full of books. Long discussions took place on religion and politics. I learned fast, drinking in every word. Over on the other side of the lough, they said, there was constant trouble between the Catholics and Protestants, but on this side they all got on great. There was injustice; there was call for civil rights, but people would work things out among themselves in time, if only the trouble-makers left them alone. Paisley was bad news but the IRA were no bargain either. Gran was always talking about the United Irishmen and how Thomas Russell, the man from God knows where, was living in Fermanagh before the 1798 Rising. He was a Protestant who was hanged for the 'cause', which is the same thing as civil rights, all Irish men and women pulling together without fear or favour. From listening to my granny I learned off by heart a long poem about him, "Into our townland on a night of snow .... The man they hanged by Downpatrick gaol was the man from God knows where". "That was Thomas Russell", Gran said, "our grandma used to tell us that she saw him once on a big grey mare in Enniskillen. He wanted the

Protestants and Catholics to unite". I was learning more and more about the Irish side of me. I missed nothing.

My first summer in Ireland, Uncle Father James came home for his holidays from the Philippines. He was Maggy's brother. What debates he had with the cayliers around the fire, about the goings-on in the world, the good and the bad, and I was listening and learning. Martin Luther King was a black clergyman marching for civil rights for the black people in America, but the red-necks hated his guts; he was putting his life on the line every time he put his head up. Bernadette Devlin was a young girl marching for civil rights for the Catholics in the North; Paisley and his Orange henchmen didn't like it one wee bit. But the listeners wanted to hear about the Philippines. I was all ears. He explained that most of the people were tenants on their own land, exactly the way it was in Ireland in the time of the landlords. A group called the Grand Alliance were out for land reform there, good men. They knew more than he did about Davitt and Parnell and Gladstone and the Irish land acts. They had just been joined by a man called Ferdinand Marcos; a tricky playboy, he called him, out for himself. They'd have to watch him. Fr. James said he knew Marcos well; he was married to a girl by the name of Imelda Romualdez who used to sing in their church choir in Tacloban on the island of Leyte. Uncle Fr. James said he wouldn't trust either of them as far as he could throw them; they were out for themselves. Story after story far into the night and no one got up to go. He told how the people loved Ramon Magsaysay who fought the Communist Huks, and became the President of the Philippines, and died in a plane crash in Cebu on St. Patrick's Day, 1957. Fr. James could grip you with his yarns. He said Marcos came from up in Ilocos near China and was part Chinese. His father had a fierce running feud with another politician called Nalundasan. When Marcos was fifteen his father was insulted by Nalundasan in an election speech. That night Nalundasan was brushing his teeth at the window before going to bed and young Ferdie shot him stone-

16

dead from a mile away with a telescopic rifle. And on and on, and I was all ears.

What a time we had that week; it flew like the wind. The weather seemed to be mostly blustery and sunny that summer with an odd sun-shower, and he took me with him everywhere he went. All the locality around Gran Ketty's place is water and islands and low hills, but over from Goladuff only a few miles as the crow flies there is a little mountain of bare rock rising straight out of the lough. It is called St. Ninny's Hill. One night when the weather was calm Uncle Father James said, "I borrowed an engine; we'll go over to Ninny's Hill tomorrow". So we were up at cock-crow and the three of us headed out across the lough and climbed to the top of the little mountain. We sat on the warm flagstones gazing out dreamily over the miles of water shining like a mirror and the deep green shadows under the tree fringes and the golden path away to the shore under where the sun sailed high. The new bridges linked Trasna island to the east and west shores. Derrylin lay slumbering below us in the heat. I can still see his finger pointing out Enniskillen in the far distance away to the left, and Lisnaskea straight across, and the castles, and Belturbet up to the right above the mouth of the river. Gran had a surprise for us, boxty dumplings. "Have another suppa tay, Shamie", she would say, gazing fondly at her priest-son. That was a magic time; I wanted to stay up there forever. Uncle Fr. James had no collar on and he was singing a song, 'Of all nature's beauties she is the queen, lovely Lough Erne and her islands so green'. From the top of the little mountain the lough looked just like a picture, with the different shapes and sizes and shades of green islands of trees painted here and there on the water. And we had a little game; he would squint at me with a funny face and say, "How's the heart?". And I would sing back at him, "Playin bumpsadaisy on me ribs". I longed to crawl into his lap and cuddle up to him and tell him my secret, but I was afraid that that would break the spell and spoil everything.

Another day he hired a car and we went down and climbed to the top of Quilca mountain, just the two of us. Another day we sailed in the cot up to see the ruins of the old castles at Quivvy and Saundersons and Crom. He took me to see the graves of the anchestors at Aghalurcher and Donagh and beside the abbey ruins on Galloon island. He was going to take me next, away over to Connemara, to show me where he had spent his seminary days. Suddenly it was all over. A phonecall arrived for him at the pub in Derrylin to go to Dublin at once. From there he flew out to Germany; as well as being a missioner, he was a chaplain in the American army. I never saw him again.

That Christmas I went to the Philippines for the first time, hoping that I might see him there. That was very different again from both Canada and Ireland; still many things also reminded me of Ireland. I was looking out the plane window: it was evening and the sun was hanging in the sky like a lamp. The pilot said we were still seven miles up when I first saw what looked for all the world like a string of lovely green jewels scattered on a shining mirror, and I thought of lovely Lough Erne and her islands so green from the top of the little mountain. When we landed in Manila what hit me first was the heat. Toronto can bake you as well as freeze you, but this was a sticky, sweaty heat coming through my clothes and sticking them to my skin. The next thing that hit me was the smell. For me every place has it's own smell; in Toronto it's car fumes, in Ireland it's turf smoke. One has to go east to get the nose educated; there each country has it's own peculiar bouquet, a cocktail rich and pungent, ranging from the sublime to the sink-hole. Manile's ripe blend hit my nose head-on. Beyond the range of human perfumes and stinks, Mother Nature had spread a paradise of delights for all the senses, great forest giants and bamboo and palms, fruit-trees and radiant flowers, wild orchids hanging like draperies down the mountainsides. Here grows the Master's masterpiece, the mango tree.

My cousins met us at the airport and I parted with my travelling companion, who was going on down to Zamboanga on

18

Mindanao. We piled into a little rattly bus called a jeepney and headed for the wharf, threading our way at a snail's pace through endless hot muddy streets of shanties. It was bedlam; milling crowds and swarms of children, and pigs and chickens everywhere, and curious odours, and horns blaring happily. Among the huge ships was a tiny one with two gangplanks. Up one families were boarding; down the other trotted an endless line of sweating men and boys, with loads on their heads far bigger than themselves. Soon the ship's whistle blew, the gangways went up and we sailed away down among the islands. By now it was pitch dark and the cicadas were strumming in full tune. The pigs and the chickens travelled on the lower deck, and the people reclined on camp beds side by side on the upper deck, some sleeping, some murmuring quietly far into the night. The moon shone on the velvety black sea, and the little ship sent showers of liquid sparks streaming out from her bows, and the flying-fish skated away on the fiery crests of the waves. I wished we could sail on forever. No sleep for me that night.

We reached the town of Barongan on the island of Samar in the early morning. Barefoot boys lined the wharf and jumped across the yawning gap on to the moving ship, to get first chance at carrying the luggage. When we landed a jeepney took us to the beach and they let me pay the driver and the money was different again; the fare was ten centavos each, about five cents in Canadian money. Tia Maria lived on an island too, the island of Ando, about three miles out in the Pacific ocean. I could see it clearly from the shore and also a canoe coming in fast to the beach. They had been expecting us and had set out when they saw the little ship rounding the headland. The canoe was long and narrow, dug out of a single log, and had what they called outriggers on both sides to keep it from turning over. Two barefoot boys, wearing only shorts and necklaces of sharks' teeth round their necks, sat on their hunkers and stroked with wide paddles.

Tia Maria's house was up on stilts and had two rooms. We slept on mats on the bamboo floor in the sala. In the other room was a tiny altar on a long wooden box. For light she had a piece of cloth stuck in a bottle of cocoanut-oil for a wick. The fire was outside. The bathroom was a walk in the woods. What a magic time was that two weeks every year on Ando. There were all kinds of birds there decked out in the colours of the rainbow, but not one of them could sing. They could only squawk. Only the hens talked the same as the Goladuff hens. I love the sounds hens make the world over; they cackle crazy when they lay an egg; they scold; they chuckle; they mutter to themselves; they natter on like a flock of women. The world would be dead without the sounds of hens.

Every evening the people would light fires along the shore to entice the fish to come inside the coral reef safe from the sharks. Then men, women and children waded into the warm sea, all the girls wearing long dresses and the boys up to ten wearing nothing at all. With baskets and leaky vessels of all sizes and shapes we scooped up the fish wriggling around our legs in the warm water. Then we sat in the firelight and the young men strummed their guitars and sang their happy and sad songs. And stories were told just like on Goladuff, "The wife sent Juan in to the mercado to sell chickens. Poor Juan drank a little tuba and lost the rest of the money. What would he do? The wife would kill him when he got home. He went into the church to pray to San Antonio to find the money for him. He went out and searched some more. No luck. Juan was getting vexed with San Antonio and started threathening him. The priest was worried for the safety of his beautiful new statue and replaced it with the little old one. The next time Juan came in, he was getting frantic. He looked up puzzled and said, "Run back in, sonny and send out your father, till I put a bit of manners on him".

There is a cave on Ando. We childen would creep in as quiet as mice to see how far we could get before the bats heard us. Then a faint drumming sound, like heavy rain falling on leaves, would start up deep in the cave. It got louder. That was the signal and we all went flat on the floor, arms covering heads, hearts thumping; they came streaming out in their hundreds, as big as persian cats, and flittered like crazy kites high in the noon-day sky. We ran out to watch them circling over the island. They formed a big umbrella that dimmed the light into dusk. Somehow they sensed when we were all out; then they lined up in columns and streamed back into the dark caverns deep under the island. The day would come when I would muster up courage to go on in on my own on tiptoe and see them hanging from their roosts in the gloom, like clusters of black chickens hanging by their necks in the mercado.

On a shelf of rock just inside the mouth of the cave were some big Chinese jars and bits of broken pottery and bones, neatly stacked up. The children said that when someone died the body was embalmed and kept in the house, in a long box under the altar. After seven years the body had shrunk; it was then put in one of the jars in the cave. They kept the dead close; that way they wouldn't come back to haunt them, the children said.

I never got a chance to see Uncle Father James after all; every time I was there he was away somewhere, on chaplain duty at Clark Field Airforce Base, or at the Naval Base on Subic Bay, or with the soldiers in Vietnam, or down in Mindanao. It wasn't his fault, but I was surprised that he never wrote to me, not even a card for Christmas. I never forgot him, and that wonderful week that flew with the wind, that first time when Gran Ketty was still alive and I was six.

That first time on Ando, the night before I was to leave for Toronto, I had a dream. Remember the little altar I mentioned in Tia Maria's wee house. One of the pictures on the altar was a young girl. Very pretty she was. In my dream I saw her wading in the sea in a white dress. She was singing, "Gugma ko, ngano ba intawon naglimbong ka? - My love, whyever did you forsake me?". I asked Grandma next morning who she was. "That is Esther. She died many years ago". That was all she said; then her face closed.

21

Chapter 3

Maggy died in 1971 when I was going on twelve. It was only when she was gone that I missed her. She had a big heart and was good to me in her own way. Maybe she thought all along that she had treated me the same as the others. After all I was not her own and, wherever I had turned up from, she had taken me in. I bitterly regretted, the minute she was gone, that I never had the gumption to ask her. I think she meant to tell me all along and just kept putting it off from one day to the next. Now the secret was with her in the grave. It made me all the more determined; as the priest said the prayers at the grave, I said, "Maggy, you're gone home to God; your troubles are over; mine may be only starting, but I wont stop till I get at the truth". She wasn't even cold when the rat Raul was back, throwing his weight around. He hadn't turned up for the wake or the funeral, but as soon as the hubbub died down, there he was. He cleared the open house in double quick time; after the years of bedlam the place was suddenly like a morgue.

Looking back now, I should have mustered up courage and taken someone into my confidence. But who? I had no one. Maggy had worked in the hospital; maybe there was a clue there, but I it didn't cross my mind at the time. I kept it all bottled up inside. As it turned out, my troubles were only starting. Raul wouldn't leave me alone, pestering me any time he got me on my own. I knew what he was after; knowing him, I wasn't surprised. I had to watch him like a hawk, not to get cornered. Even now I cant bear the thought of that horrible time; I still try to shut it out like a bad dream. It still turns my stomach. I kept a weather eye out for him, ear cocked for his step. Then out a window and run for dear life. I had longed to be touched; now the thought made me sick.

Night was the worst time; any excuse to sleep with the others. Often they would put me out of their room, out of pure spite, it seemed, and I would lie there awake, afraid he would steal in on me with his breath stinking and catch me asleep. My heart would jump and pound at the least sound; was it the monster on the prowl? I'd doze off; suddenly there he'd be, leaning over me. I'd scream bloody murder fit to waken the dead. He would hush the children, telling them I was having a nightmare. My one thought was to get away from that house, or sooner or later. he'd get me. I'd rather die. The dread of him only spurred me on the more.

Study was my only hope, the books was my lifeline; I lived for the day when I would get away and somehow start my search. Was she dead? Was that why I was left? What about my father? Was he dead too? Did he know about me? Where was the answer? In the Philippines? In Ireland? Now that Maggy was gone, that was the end of my trips to Goladuff and to Ando. But somehow I always felt I would find a way, that God was on my side. I'm an optimist.

I was lucky to have a great teacher by the name of Mrs. Markowitz who took me under her wing. She pushed me; the odd time I felt down or slacked off a bit, she lifted me with that cheery voice of hers, "Terry, you can do it. You can get a scholarship to college, but to get a full scholarship, you have to be an all-rounder". Sometimes I would turn up breathless on her doorstep, with a cock-and-bull story about homework. The good, innocent woman had never heard the definition of a virgin in the Philippines, 'A twelve-year-old girl who can run faster than a forty-year-old man'. Her son Tommy was a year older than me. We started to study together and we became good friends, as long as he kept his hands to himself. Poor Tommy, he couldn't make me out. I suppose at the time I had him mixed up in my head with Raul. If he made a move I cut him dead; no hanky-panky for me. Poor Tommy got several whacks; we fell out; we made up. Our worst row was the night he got so frustrated that he hinted I was a lesbian and got a black eye for his pains. He knew I never even had a girl-friend. I always liked Tommy. Some day, I would say, but not yet. Poor

23

Tommy has the patience of Job. That was the night we sterilised his mother's hat-pin and pricked our wrists and made a solemn pact in blood. He calls me his cold-fish; he sure needs that sense of humour of his. He is still my best friend, but even to him, I couldn't bring myself to reveal my unfinished business.

No lovelife for Terry but I was into everything else, the school paper, the swimming team, debating, class president, you name it. I slaved at the books. They called me an over-achiever, a swat, a nerd, the brain, not knowing what drove me. I came out tops in my class, with a full scholarship good enough even for the likes of Harvard or Yale. I picked Hofstra in Queens, Long Island. It is Jewish. Again Mrs. Markowitz was there with her support and sound advice. Hofstra was her alma mater; unlike the smug, self-centred ivy-league set-up catering to an elite, it had a worldwide reputation of being a topclass cosmopolitan university, which excluded no one from the human family. Where better could a Canadian-Irish-Filipina mestiza redhead feel at home? I was on my way. At seventeen I knew exactly where I was going, what I wanted, to find my roots. I would study these two brands of human animal, to see what made them tick. College life for me wasn't for kicking my heels; This was serious business. I was getting ready to hunt the world for a needle in a haystack.

Hofstra in the mid-70s was a great place to be, a kind of intel-lectual oasis in the great American desert. Even Toronto has some depth compared to New York. No fairminded person would question the superiority of the American computer brain, but Americans dont think, in any real sense of the word. America doesn't read; it scans big headlines and chases fads and instant stimuli. Thinking is hard work; it is painful, terrify-ing; it is possible only in a mind that is free from ingrained big-otry, that loves the truth above all treasure. Americans have no interest in the rest of the human family except as raw material. The lowliest redneck thinks he is a blue-blooded aristocrat, that the world belongs to him by divine right. Ivy-league cult is parochial, fixated on it's own navel. That's why Mrs.

Markowitz urged me to choose Hofstra, one of the few windows in that pampered ivory tower, looking out on the real world where the other half lives. Democracy American style is a cynical luxury of the new aristocracy, a very sick joke. Capitalists are petty hucksters become the new robber barons above all law. Their god is mammon. They have prostituted their glorious democracy. They have hearts of granite. Their messiah is Harry Truman dropping the bomb on Japan. These mighty he-men make me sick; they give democracy and decent Americans a bad name.

This gut feeling kept me going, that somewhere out there I would some day get lucky and stumble on a clue to my personal mystery. A shot in the dark, a wildgoose chase surely, but it was the only way I knew. I just had to prepare myself and keep searching till I found out who I was. You have to understand that I was starting from scratch, now that Maggy was gone. I couldn't confront Raul; Hofstra was my hope.

As I said, Mrs. Markowitz was Jewish and had gone to Hofstra herself, so she naturally recommended her alma mater, and for that I will be eternally grateful to her. I felt at home there from the first. Jews and Irish and Filipinos have much in common; all three have a history of dual persecution under bigots, with the sword in one hand and the cross in the other. During my first year there, my focus gradually crystallised. I would study history, get to know my two peoples better. I would study psychology, get to know something about the sins of the fathers and the mothers. It was study with a vengeance and a purpose. I was consciously laying the foundation, the only way I knew, to find my roots, to find her. Some day, with God's help, I would hit on a clue. I figured a good detective had to do his homework to be able to spot a lead when he saw one. Fear drove me; fear that my mother's shadow might fall on me and I might miss it if my eye wasn't sharp enough. She might be keening in the night and I might not hear her, if my ear was not in tune. Looking back now, I have much to be thankful to God for. He has held me in the hollow of his hand, and brought me safe through all the tangles. How else did I, such a ean corr, as they say in Irish, survive all the snares of the fowler?

Henry Ford is laughed at for his crass summary of the human story, 'History is bunkum'. Do you know, he didn't know how right he was in a way. I agree with him, but in an altogether different sense from the way he was thinking. All written history is biased, edited, a hodge-podge of half-truths and barefaced lies, for the very simple reason that it is written by the winner with a purpose, to justify conquest and oppression and the denigration and obliteration of the native culture. Julius Caesar had no conscience, no more than Ghengis Khan, but your modern white aggressor has to convince himself that he is doing people a favour as he rapes and robs them. The conquered and the colonised have no luxuries like pen and ink; they leave no records. The only history worth a damn has to be read between the lines. Hofstra was the place to dig deep into the real story of my two peoples, one the colony of England, the other the colony of Spain. Interlaced into both sagas was the tangled web woven by the churchmen in the name of the good God. To me it was highly significant that we were required at Hofstra to master enough Latin to be able to read simple church Latin, if we wanted to do a degree in history.

Another thing I learned at Hofstra was that I was not unique in having no parents, or rather, in not knowing who my parents were. That in itself was a breakthrough, an eye-opener, a mighty boulder lifted off my soul. I wasn't a pariah after all; I had kindred spirits from gawas sa muscatero, even famous people like Marilyn Monroe and Willy Brandt, the mayor of Berlin, and Blessed Eamonn De Valera himself, if the truth be told. It was half the battle to discover that there was nothing fundamentally wrong with me after all. It was not my fault; what a relief it was to get out from under the load of guilt. Then I met a girl who had been adopted. What a wonderful thing it was to be able to talk to another human being about my terrible, secret birthmark. Her adoptive parents had told her the truth from the start, but she said there was no chance of ever finding her real parents. I said, "Hope springs eternal; one never knows". I'm an optimist.

What goes for psychology I found superficial, of little use for my purpose. They try to make sense of the mystery on human terms; dogmatically and unscientifically omitting the one most important element in the equation, the possibility of the divine. Freud has many insights into human nature, but his explaining everything that makes people tick, simply by the sex drive, is puerile. The human animal is a great deal more complicated than that. Only Frankl's insight, that the goal-drive is the key to the human animal, stands up. Man must have a meaning and purpose in life; that made sense to me, and had stark relevance to my own situation. This was no mere theory; the man had survived four years in the Nazi concentration camps of Auschwitz and Dachau on the strength of it, where his wife and children, his parents and brother, had been exterminated. I came to my own conclusions. Unlike any other animal, the human can view the future with purpose; can hope; can look for meaning; can love. This is conscience, call it what you will. When the human male chooses to abandon his true aim, he reverts to brute force, like the other animals. But they only kill to eat. Man becomes a loose cannon, kills by syndrome, a maniac with a scatter-gun, for the pure heck of it. The woman connives and concurs in the male's aggression, simply for the sake of survival. Tribal man's solution to every problem is, and has always been, bury the so-and-so. How the syndrome got started is the mystery, the facts behind the Bible story are carried in our genes.The pattern is repeated inexorably and re-enforced by each succeeding generation; like father, like son; like mother, like daughter, good and bad. The only power that can break this syndrome of sin-hate-kill is the love of God poured into our hearts, inviting and empowering each one individually to convert, to turn away from the evil and love the good. The record is there, plain to any open mind, that we have in us a strong inclination to evil. Progress my eye! Jesus is the bridge, the way to becoming truly human, which is our destiny. Love is our only hope, and that includes loving oneself. Christ is the divine wizard; his magic alone can break the spell. Others, like the Buddha, have seen the light; only the Son of Man has the power to change the human heart, if we let him. Wimps say there is no God and wallow in hedonism like pigs in shit. Open your eyes. He is walking in the garden on two human feet..

Will we ever become fully human, truly civilised, sharing this planet, playing fair in peace and harmony? Or are we going to blow it up and exterminate ourselves and all on it? We may have a chance, if the real women, not the women who ape men, take over. Woman's heart is compassionate, like God's. Women do not march to war. But, in church and state, macho man will not give up power, until he's brought to his knees. Maybe that is what God is at; woman is the Omega Point, modelled on his human masterpiece, Mother Mary.

The accumulated residue of all the sins of all the fathers and the mothers back to the beginning is original sin. It's bred in the bone. Shakespeare wrestles with it all the time in his tragedies. Hence the contradiction that the more we advance in power, the more we sin against our neighbour. If we dont love, we destroy. Love is the most abused word in the English language. The real thing is not mushy; it means fair play in the heart. Grace is our only hope; that is the promise which became incarnate in Jesus, which becomes incarnate in me, provided I open my heart to it, the miracle of metanoia, change of heart, that John the Baptist heralded. "If anyone will open the door, I will come in .." is the promise. It says in Jeremiah, ch. 31, v.29, "In those days they shall say no more: 'The fathers have eaten sour grapes, and the children's teeth are set on edge". Religion is not piety for wimps; it is the very stuff of life, our only hope.The eye must be single; it's all about aim. The human will, aided by God's grace, can cut through the syndrome of evil; otherwise it is re-inforced and free-wheels on down the line. The Son of Man knew his psychology; it is the human heart that is the source of all sorrow in the world. Where did I fit into the picture?

There weren't many Filipinos in Hofstra then but enough to enable me to form a couple of warm friendships. The Philippine people are the salt of the earth. Raul was a glugger, one of the very few bad eggs that proved the rule. They took me to their hearts; I was one of their own; genuinely interested, not patronising, unbigoted, speaking their language. Like all exploited peoples, they have suffered under the poisonous cloud of the white man's arrogant superiority; treat a Filipino as an equal and you can do no wrong; you have a friend for life, who wouldn't think twice of putting his life on the line for you. I had a good head-start; a Filipina with flaming red hair is a rare bird indeed. On the other hand, the Irish contingent was strong in numbers, and I made some genuine friends among them too. But they were mostly rowdy, drunken, spoiled brats; the sons and daughters of narrowbacks who had sold their birthright for the American dream and made a killing. There is a Latin saying, corruptio optimi pessima; it fits the Irish like a glove; when they are good, they are the salt of the earth; when they're bad, they stink to high heaven. The Irish have more layers to them than an onion.

My scholarship covered basic expenses only, so I needed a job. Again, like a stray cat flung out a window, I landed on my feet; no one wanted to work in the stuffy library, and that was just my cup of tea. Here I could delve to my heart's content, and get paid a few bucks for it. The old librarian, Sid, had been in Auswitz, and he loved books. I had no entanglements; as far as Raul and the others were concerned, I didn't exist. That suited me. My red hair caught many an eye; I got my share of mating displays, but all were kept at arm's length. No love-life for me just yet; I had a lust of my own, to catch a glimpse of my lost childhood, back down the long vista of memory.

Hofstra was a happy time, up to a point, for I had a goal in life; an obsession would be more like it. But the bastard''s is a lonely road. My heart felt not broken so much as torn. The emptiness inside me drove me on. How I resented the enjoyment I couldn't join. Oh to be young and care-less and fancyfree. Oh to be a whole person, to be normal. The odd time I went into a bar, I pitied the poor slobs drinking themselves stupid. Anger welled up inside me at the one-night stands, that could so easily leave another lost child ploughing a lone furrow. But I pitied myself too, when I went back cold sober to my lone bed. They called me the brain. They said I was an arrogant bitch. They said I was frigid. They wondered what made Terry run. How can any normal person know what it feels like to be a cypher with no name, a question-mark even to oneself? An orphan loses father and mother and that is terrible, but at least there's some kind of memory, a name, a picture, some link, if only the grave. I was illegitimate, as if I wasn't born at all, a soul in limbo. Nobody likes to be called a bastard; nobody knows how it feels to be one. Where did I come from? Why? What? Who? Did two lonely people look across a crowded room? Was it two strangers in the night? Am I the fruit of love at first sight, or of an act of lust, or of savage, bestial rape? Was I a stand-up job, my genesis pickled in alcohol?. My faith in God kept me going. Some day I would find out. Serendipity is not blind chance or the toss of a coin; it is written in the stars from the start, by the finger of God.

I was ever on the alert for a lead. Sometimes I saw myself as a lonewolf prospector who finds a gold flake here, a flash in the pan there, to keep him going. One day he'll hit the mother-lode; hey presto, the jackpot. The hunter may be after hares and rise a fox instead, or stumble on a cock-pheasant, who puts the heart crossways in him with an explosion of wings. You cant pick and choose between ghosts from the past. In my quest for my holy grail. I was like an old hound casting about for the scent. Nosing into every musty nook and cranny, I came across many a fascinating relic.

One time I was poking around in the library of an abandoned monastery, in a place called Oconamawoc up along the west bank of the Hudson, and came across a heap of old volumes. Buried under out-of-date textbooks was an ancient tome with uncut pages, on the Spanish Inquisition, written in church

Latin. That was an eye-opener, reading between the lines of course. Here and there I found the odd juicy tid-bit on the Philippines.

Item: Ferdinand Majellan set out to sail around the world and stumbled on this totally unknown archipelago, or sea of islands, in the western Pacific in 1521. He thought he had found the Spice Islands and had it made. With half-a-dozen soldiers in armour, he got himself embroiled in a local skirmish on the island of Opon, near Cebu in the central islands, thinking naively that their armour made them invincible. But a local hero called Lapu Lapu, clad only in a loincloth, found a chink in the armour with his poisoned arrow, and it was lights out for Majellan. He's still on Opon.

Item: When the Spaniards came back in 1565 they claimed and named the archipelago of over seven thousand islands for King Philip. Nor did they stand on ceremony or ask many questions; they conquered and converted the natives who survived the massacre, in the one smooth operation. No record of martyrs, if any. Mass baptism was the order of the day. Before 1565 was out the Philippines was one hundred per cent Catholic, not counting aborigines and Moslems.

So western civilisation/christianity came to the Philippines. The Spaniards left the Moslems in Mindanao severely alone, apart from christening them Moros, after their old enemies back home across the Straits of Gibraltar in Morocco. They had had their bellyful of Moros.

Item: The Philippines became a dumping-ground for the Spanish church. Priests who got in trouble with the Inquisition back in Spain were first shipped to Mexico. If that didn't settle them, their next sea-cruise took them to Manila. Some were such hot potatoes that Manila couldn't hold them and they were shipped south to such God-forsaken outposts as Samar and Leyte, where they went completely native. That had a familiar ring to it; the stories recounted in no. 7, Sudbury St., of priests who followed the native custom of taking a wife and siring large families, had a long and venerable history.

Item: The Spaniards might be no-bodies back in Spain, but from the instant they set foot in the Philippines they were blue-blooded grandees to a man; they might be street sweepers back home; here they treated the Filipinos like dirt. It was over a hundred and fifty years before they ordained the first native priest, and they did so only under duress, not from the Vatican mind you, but because of a direct order from the Spanish King. It took a hundred years more before a Filipino priest rose above the rank of a lowly curate. In the year 1800 they still did not have one bishop of their own. The Philippines has had thousands of saintly men and woman. I have met some of them. To this day, not one of them has been canonised by Rome. Another racket, like relics and indulgences .... This was the Catholic ancestry one half of me had come from.

What about the other half of me? One time I was up in East Durham in Green County in the Catskills, the home-from-home of the New York Irish. It was coming up to St. Patrick's Day and the Friendly Sons were running a concert. A frail old priest with white hair played some tunes for us on the fiddle. I struck up a chat with him. While we talked, I was admiring the beautiful violin and the gold mountings on the bow. He looked at me slyly out of a wee face as wizened as an old frosted apply and said, "You'd never guess, girly, who it belonged to. Liam Mellows no less, a martyr for Ireland. You know, he was in the Rising and stayed with us when he was on the run from the British. We hid him and a cache of arms under the altar, over in Orange County".

Another time I went to Mass with friends in a seminary chapel near Sing Sing. The sermon didn't set me on fire and my attention wandered up to the stained glass window above my head. Were my eyes deceiving me? There, among the haloed saints and scholars, was none other than the Long Fella, Dev himself, in a bevy of bishops, looking very much at home and as saintly as you please. No mistaking that beaked nose and the ascetic specs and the brow of destiny. And he was sporting a halo with the best of them.

Then there was the time I was rooting around in a second-hand book-shop in the city and came across a book by Thomas MacDonagh published in the spring of 1916, just before Easter week. A piece of faded yellow paper fell out, a page of a hand-written letter from a ghost :-

Turlough, Rosmuck,
Co. Galway.
12th Aug. 1914.

A chara dilis,

I have come back here after a few busy days in Dublin, and send you the following chronicle of events.

First, to remove some misimpressions which I and others may have given you. I think I told you that the number of guns landed at Howth was 2,500, and Tom Clarke in his cable to "G.S." says 2,000. We have both exaggerated, relying on rumour. The actual number was only 900. The number landed at Kilcool was only 600. This gives 1,500 in all. They are 11 mm. Mausers of a rather antiquated pattern, without magazines, and are much inferior to the British service rifle and even to those which Carson's men have. Moreover, the ammunition landed is useless. It consists of explosive bullets, wh. are against the rules of civilised war, and wh. therefore ....

(on the reverse side of the page) .... clear that whatever is to be done for Ireland in this crisis must be done outside the Prov. Comtee. The men are sound, especially in Dublin. We cd. at any moment rally the best of them to our support by a coup d'etat; and rally the whole country if a coup d'etat were successful. But a coup d'etat while the men are unarmed in unthinkable.

The British Govt. will arm and train us if we come under the War Office & accept the C.-in C. in Ireland as our generalissimo. Detailed plans are already drawn up and have been tentatively submitted. So far, the Prov. Comtee. is unanimously against it. But if Redmond directs them to submit? Then, I think, the split will come.

I am sending a letter in similar terms to McGarrity. Do not use any of this for publication.

Sincerely yours

P. H. Pearse.

To the best of my knowledge, the existence of this fragment of a letter from Pearse to John Devoy in New York is otherwise unknown. The things one stumbles on in the chase, the thrills of serendipity.

For a bastard I had my share of personal luck too; the day came when a lovely plum fell into my lap as if by magic. The career of Ed Morrow, the WW 2 correspondent, had always fascinated me. If only I could find a job like that. I didn't know Ted Turner from Adam, but one day I happened to see a piece on him in the New York Times. He was rich beyond counting. He raced yachts for a hobby. He had won the Americas Cup for the United States. He had bought a baseball team. The article said Turner was off and running again with a new idea; he was planning to set up a worldwide news network. He was going to break the mould. Up till then, the TV networks, the so-called big three, ABC, CBS and NBC, operated on the accepted premise that the US is the world. That's where the action is; the rest is not newsworthy, only small potatoes, mere piddling trivia beneath the notice of God's great master race. Who cares about the lesser breed without the law, except as a source of raw materials for building the empire?. Turner realised that there are people out there; he was going world-wide. I had an interview set up before I graduated, and I made sure to have my homework done. That was how I got in on the ground floor with CNN in Atlanta, Georgia.

I'm now three years at it, covering the hot spots, Africa, Asia, South America, Europe, you name it. No sooner does the fire die down in one hotspot than it flares up in another, Angola, Nicaragua, the Gaza Strip, East Timor, Chile. And I'm reading between the lines; telling it like it is. Big business sells arms to both sides. Big business puts the squeeze on Uncle Sam and Uncle Sam does what he's bid. I report the official news, tongue in cheek, for I see what's happening every day with my own two eyes. As far as man's humanity to man goes, that's for the birds. I am a dyed-in-the-wool cynic. But that's all neither here nor there; I had not for one moment lost sight of my own agenda. For nearly a year now I am CNN's special correspondent for two special hotspots, the Philippines and Northern Ireland, PI and NI for short. I wangled it because I'm an Irish-Filipina with the local argot and an inside track in both. I have been in Belfast and Manila at least ten times. I am on a first-name basis with Imelda and Ferdie and Paisley and Hume, equally at home in Quezon City and Derry. And I may have stumbled on something at last, the faintest whiff of a scent. Something tells me I'm getting warm.

I was in Manila last spring and took a couple of days off and went back to Ando again. I have always been curious about the big wooden casket under the altar in Tia Maria's house. The picture of the girl in white was still on the altar. I asked Tia Maria casually was the girl still there inside. She looked startled. "No", she answered slowly, "she is now in the cave. When they brought her home --", and she stopped and said no more. I asked her when exactly Esther had died and she couldn't remember. Why was she being so secretive, so evasive? It took a little patience and a few pesos to a local paisano for tuba, but I got my answer. Esther died in Canada, he said. Back in Toronto it didn't take long to get the record; Esther died on the 7th of June, 1960, the day after I was born. Is that merely a coincidence?

In July I was in the North of Ireland to cover the Twelfth. The way I see it, both Protestants and Catholics are the victims of Britain's colonialism. None of the churches have had the courage to break the syndrome, to set an example, beyond polite, meaningless words. It's the old control thing all over again. If an Orange parade is a celebration of Protestant culture, God help them. It was the professor with the specs and the brow of destiny who gave the IRA their divine right. I finally got away from the madness and headed for Connemara, to visit at last the place Uncle Father James had raved about, all those years ago. He is not Father James any more, if the rumours are correct. Gran Ketty is long dead. There is not a soul left on Goladuff only poor old Robby, crippled with arthritis. He knew nothing. The story goes that Uncle James left the priesthood and got married after his mother died, and that he is living somewhere in the western United States. Did he know anything about Esther? One of these days I'm going to get on his trail. Who knows, he might have something to tell me.

I drove at my leisure out through Spiddal along the coast and found Pearse's cottage in Rosmuck. Very lonely. Very sad. On around by Roundstone and up towards Clifden, I was in a sombre mood in keeping with the landscape in the haunting twilight. Out on a headland I spotted a graveyard, the headstones etched against the still-bright ocean. I stopped the car and walked over and sat on the graveyard wall, ruminating about nothing in particular, listening to the pulse of the slow-breathing sea. An old man came along, leading a small dark cow on a rope. Neither of them seemed in any more hurry than I was, so, while the cow browsed, we sat on the wall and exchanged comments. He produced a plug of black tobacco from a waistcoat pocket and bit off a chaw. Once the weather was out of the way, we got down to the real stuff, mutual curiosity. He wanted to hear all about me and my travels, and he had plenty to tell too, for he had travelled in his time, and he read a lot. He happened to mention that tourists sometimes wanted to see the grave of the turncoat priest buried here at Ballyconneely, and he fired a powerful brown spit in the direction of a tall tombstone tilted at an angle. That must have been what put the young monks into his head and my antenna shot up, bristling; "They never went home in them days. They used to arrive in droves every year at the end of June at the big house beyant. For five weeks they were all over land and sea like hordes of black pismires, cycling, walking, climbing, swimming, fishing. but they never opened their mouths, never spoke to a soul. They're gone, aye this twenty year". The dun cow was getting restless; it was past her milking-time. The Connemaraman, with his tobacco cud, bade me godspeed and set out to follow the trailing rope home and I went a-hunting.

It was getting dark and the sea mist was rolling in from the Atlantic when I found the place, away out on another headland. The gardens were over-grown; even in the deepening night I could see that they have been beautiful once. The big old house had had bits and pieces added on. Windows boarded up, it stood now a blind, lonesome sentinel facing the west. The sea-gulls and the mother ewes were calling out of the mist. I wandered through the stables and tested the straw mattresses the young monks had slept on. A cowl appearing across the yard would not have greatly surprised me. Extending from the main house was an oblong structure of cinder-block with an asbestos roof, it's ugliness in stark contrast to the main house; mercifully the ivy would soon completely cover it's naked shame.

I had little trouble finding a way in; I never go out without my jemmy; it wouldn't be my first breaking-and-entering into a house of the dead. As my eyes got used to the gloom, I saw it was the refectory; the platters still laid out on the trestle tables for the next meal. Laudetur Jesus Christus, in big block letters, hung askew over the reader's rostrum. Through the dark passage I groped my way into the house. All but two rooms had wooden cots with straw mattresses and a crucifix on the bare wall. Under the stairs I found a box of old books, Latin and Greek textbooks and a couple in Irish in the old spelling. At the very bottom was a bundle of Browne and Nolan copy-books of different colours, tied up with a length of string. These I took; who knows what they might tell me? and was on my way.

In the B&B I undid the string, mildly curious. The six exercise books were marked from 1 to 6 on the front cover. Inside, all six were filled with numbers. What on earth ...? My first thought was, a gambler, a runner for the numbers game in New York City, but these numbers didn't add up; they went across the page, not down. Could it be some kind of code? That was it. This was getting interesting; anything worth hiding had to be worth uncovering. But how to crack the code? I phoned Sid at Hofstra and told him my problem. His answer was instant; "Try the dictionary. That's the usual source; the numbered diagrams beside certain words. Dictionaries have copied one another from the time of Dr. Johnson". He was spot on. It took a while; when I reached the word 'horse', with the diagram facing left alongside and the horse's points numbered, starting at the top of the head and reading clockwise, 1 poll (p), 2 ear (e), 3 mane (m), 4 withers (w), etc. it all fell into place just like a jig-saw puzzle. It was a coded, cryptic shorthand, the barest essentials. Translating was painstakingly slow at first, a letter, a word at a time; once I got the hang of it and a little practice, it got to be as simple as church Latin. This was fun, as the digits turned into letters, and the letters into words and sentences before my eyes. Soon I could take it in without changing gears in my head, as I recognised the same patterns repeated over and over. For two months now I have been at it every spare minute. The day came, as happens with all languages, when I could read it like the newspaper, without having to transpose.

It turned out to be a kind of journal, with random entries. Here was a country lad with a compulsion to write and good reason for keeping his thoughts to himself. Like Alice falling down the rabbit-hole, through these pages I had stumbled into another world, not so wonderful but no less fantastic.: -

Chapter 4

12.8.49 : Arrived here yesterday, 25 of us from 12 counties. Met at the station by a jolly giant and a leprechaun in a wee bedford lorry. Drove out through the bog to a grey castle between two long banks of gravel. The back of beyond. All 25 of us stood in the bed of the lorry; we were lifers. The smokers took their last drags. Total silence broken by a Kerry accent; lo, a rara avis, a long-headed Kerryman with a sense of humour. He's christening; the giant bouncing on mighty buttocks in the cab is Mrs. Finn; the leprachaun is Puck .... The grub is great; the coffee-smell met us at the gate. Slept on straw. The cell has a crucifix, a table and a chair, a skull, two spiked bracelets, and a whip ... Mrs. Finn is the novice master; we are the novices. We do what he says. It's bye-bye, Bessy; I'm letting on I'm writing this to you. I'm determined but it's tough, parting with you for ever and facing this. Not yet 2 days and it already seems an eternity since we said goodbye. Fare you well, my love; I'm not even supposed to be thinking of you any more. It's a terrible risk writing this; you remember when you and I got caught before. But I have to write it to keep sane; am hiding it in the straw tick.

17.8.49 : Mrs. Finn is heavy on the sarcasm; calls us a bunch of bowzies; says we eat like bogmen. Our first lesson in priesting is table manners. He's right there, though he comes from the bog himself; I happen to know. He's teaching us how to eat like humans, small bites, chew slowly, swallow; then a sip. He's breaking us off the cement-mixer method, shovel and slosh. You learn fast here; Joxer forgot and dined solo, on his knees in the middle of the refectory floor in front of the whole community .... Early start here; bell is boss; up at half-five; last signal ten. Cold-water shave minus mirror. Full day; meditation, office, Mass, thanksgiving, breakfast of porridge, homemade bread and butter and glorious coffee. No study or profane reading allowed in this spiritual year. No talking outside recreation-time. Every waking minute is filled with prayers, meditation, spiritual reading, office, stations, manual labour, 15 decades of rosary, chapter of faults. I like siesta. The second morning Puck the leprachaun arrived with a pair of sheep-shears and scalped every man-jack of us to the bone; it's called the tonsure. Puck was grinning and I was looking down sadly at my beautiful golden curls in the multi-coloured sea of hair. We look for all the world like a flock of jail-birds, though never a soul sees us in this God-forsaken bog. Mrs. Finn rubbed in the salt, 'Vanity of vanities and all is vanity'; we must turn our backs on the sinful world of pleasure. Goodbye to the quiff ... He explained modesty of the eyes; keep eyes down; dont look at females,(no sight or sound of a woman anywhere since we arrived; there is a perimeter fence; no non-male can get within an ass's roar of the place). Next lesson; forget home; one letter allowed per month .... We are puzzled; last night we had to stay in the chapel after night prayers. The monks went to their side of the monastery; lights out; then the chanting started up in Latin. Beating time with the chanting we could here a swishing sound, like a man threshing oats with a flail. In the name of God, what were they at? It stopped; we went to our cells. I lay awake for hours, listening to the clock in the tower telling the hours and the halves. What have I got myself into? What am I doing here? A jumble of thoughts; God called me; I want to be a priest; too late now to turn back; how could I face the neighbours back home, a spoiled priest? But this ? It's good and bad; some of it so beautiful, some of it mad.

25.8.49 : We have learned a lot about this strange life in a fortnight. Mrs. Finn opens our letters; yesterday in the chapter of faults, he read out Jughead's letter home to his mother, "Spell porridge, you stupid bowzie; down on your knees" .... The Kerryman has nicknames on everybody; he's Mutt and I'm Jeff.

1.9.49 : Mrs. Finn took us out on a cross-country gallop to swim in the river Suck. The reeds were eight feet high; I never saw the river, though Mutt claimed he glimpsed water; true, his long head was higher. We barely managed to get our feet wet in the slob-lands. Marching back at the head of the column, Mrs. Finn announced he would build us a swimming-pool. "We will build him a swimming-pool", muttered Mutt, and we watched the giant buttocks swaying up ahead ... Another eye-opener; the Master, alias Mrs. Finn, started talking about the discipline. "Do you know what the discipline is?", he asked slyly. Some thought it was rules and regulations; I said I thought it meant self-control. Not here, it's doesn't. The discipline is the strange swishing sound that goes with the chanting in the dark. That's what the wee whip hanging in each cell is for; it's not just a visual reminder of the Lord's passion; a few sharp skelps will bring mortification closer to home. We're not sure of the exact details yet; do we pair off and whack each other or what? And where? We'll soon find out; to-night's the night. Not exactly as romantic as an oldtime waltz, Bessy; that's what you and I would be doing to-night if I was home. I wonder how did Cavan do in the semi-final; Ma forgot to mention it in her letter.

2.9.49 : We had our first taste of the discipline; it's simple, nothing to it. Lights out and the seven penitential psalms strike up, verse and verse about, upstairs-downstairs. There's a swing and a lilt to it and you whack away in tune to the rhythm with your whip on your own bare bottom. It's an ancient custom among monks, as old as Christianity. I'm told the Irish monks brought it to a fine art; one gets the knack in no time, whack, whack, left, right, on the two cheeks of your arse, to the rhythm of the night. I had the hang of it right away. Nothing is more natural; the human animal can adapt to anything. Mrs. Finn tells us it may be a bit severe on the body, but a tonic for the soul. "After all, the weapon is in your own hand", he comforted us on the eve of battle, for we were a wee bit nervous, not knowing what to expect. But of course, you have to let down your trousers. One of the raw recruits forgot that step in the exercise. The master has a great sense of humour; this morning at chapter he wanted to know who was playing the muffled drums last night. Mutt thinks the music is a bit dated; instead of Latin psalms, what about beating our bottoms to the tune of Red Tails in the Sunset? .... Mrs. Finn explained that the discipline is based on the principle that 'the spirit is willing but the flesh is weak'; bad thoughts, temptations of the flesh, impure desires, have proved the downfall of many a priestly vocation. He was telling us about St. Aloysius Gonzaga. He was such a holy youth that he never looked at his mother's face again, after he joined the Jesuits. Bessy love, I can see your face this minute, as plain as if I was looking at you. If I hit a wee bit harder the next time, will you go away? ..... The Master has his eye on poor wee Jeff; brought me in for a heart-to-heart chat; it's called colloquium; not about temptation exactly but about pride and self-will; what it amounts to is that a monk must be humble with no mind of his own. The arrogant monk will fall into the devil's snare. Self-will will be my downfall, he prophecies, with a watery eye. The other novices seem to have taken to this regime like ducks to water. Have they any secret thoughts, I wonder? Mutt is a born bachelor; I doubt if a woman's face ever swam across his ken .... All this will pass; only nine years more and I'll be away off on the foreign missions. P.S. I hope you're not confused; Mutt christened the Master Mrs. Finn that first day, even before the bedford started up at the station. You probably didn't know Finn McCool married a Kerrywoman who was a holy terror. That's why he was always off hunting the wild boar up on Slieve Bloom, or following the hounds chasing the bald deer through the woods along Lough Lene, or driving away the Romans from our shores. Any excuse to get away from under the lash of her tongue. No escape for poor Jeff; he has made his bed; he must lie in it.

8.9.49 : We got the habit today. And our new names. From now on each one is Bro, followed by a saint's name. I'm officially Bro Polycarp from now on, God bless the mark. As the man said when the priest christened his son Fursey, "I doubt, Father, will it shtick to him?". The Kerryman is Melchisadech. Unofficially, he and I will always be Mutt and Jeff. What was wrong with the names we got at baptism? Another step in the process aiming at anonymity; another link with humanity severed; we picked the names out of a hat. I wonder who's in the All-Ireland. Mutt, doing the buffoon, asked if we could listen to the All-Ireland. Mrs Finn thought it a great joke and let out with a rollicking bellylaugh that shook the layers of fat up and down and sideways on him. For recreation we go out for a country walk in silence, eyes glued to the ground if we meet a native. Females are a terrible danger to one's vocation; dont look. How could one face home a spoiled priest in the eyes of the parish, if one lost one's vocation?

15.9.49 : In spite of all the 'donts' and 'downers', this is a wonderful place, so peaceful, so beautiful, especially at this time of year. We are the chosen, the privileged ones; very few get a chance like this in the Ireland of today; no worries here about food or clothes or a roof over one's head. I have a cushy life here, compared to my brothers and sisters, who have to go abroad to England and Canada to make a living. Here one can be alone with God; no hurry or bustle; getting to know Jesus as a person casts out the fear. The birds are quiet now; nature is silent; silence is a friend; letting the mad, busy world go by. I can see through this cult of fear; I wont let it spoil the goodness of this life. I can see the Master is not a bad sort at heart; he is putting on a bit of an act; he feels he must follow a system hand-ed down. These are our rites of initiation, as in any tribal sys-tem. The aim seems to be to mould conformists, to eliminate individuality. I read somewhere about the rigours of 'bootcamp' in the US marines; the aim there is to produce efficient fighting-machines .... Two ways of training a young horse; break him or teach him; talk softly, touch gently, or beat him around the head with an ash-plant; terrorise him or win him. Jesus' way was to draw people by the gentle bands of love, 'Come follow me'. This way here is by breaking the spirit, grinding one down, belittling, the put-down. Mother Teresa of Avila did not treat her young nuns with contempt, like dirt, to make them humble. I can see the effect; the novices' brains stop functioning; they mope around like zombies. I watch the process; I can see through it; they are being dehumanised; already the clerical airs and graces are taking over, that suave, impersonal veneer of the professional clergyman, "my dear man, my good woman". I take it all with a grain of salt; mum's the word; it's the price we have to pay to reach the goal. Methinks Mutt and Jeff, each in his own very different way, will emerge unscathed.

43

25.9.49 : Mrs Finn feels we are woefully short on culture and has started a crash course of classical music for cavemen. God knows we need it. Reams of Mozart, Beethoven, Haydn, Bach. He has us picking out the musical instruments from Peter and the Wolf; "That's not the clarinet, you ignoramus. Tell this bog-man, Bro Albert, what instrument that is. Of course it's the oboe. Not many oboes in the bog of Allen; the nincompoop would recognise it if it was a snipe or a corncrake, ha ha ha". The culture is rubbing off on most of us; we'll soon be up there with the best of them, with our very latest Grundig phonograph and stacks of long-playing records, McCormack, Gigli, Caruso, Maire ni Scolaigh. And we're learning about stain-glass and Evie Hone. If we survive the year, we're promised a visit to Spiddal church to see real stain-glass. We'll soon be as cultured as any Jesuit .... Wild turbulant thoughts still waylay me lying awake at night; there's a hooley on in the hall back home; you're maybe doing the Siege of Ennis this very minute. There's a bevy of young nuns in a convent not too far away; we have seen them a longe on our treks. As soon as the capo spots them, it's panic stations, "About turn; quick march", and we're off, heads down, scurrying out of danger. Maybe we should ask Mrs Finn to invite them over for a hooley. I wonder do the novice nuns indulge in the discipline? They do get scalped I know. All them lovely tresses.

3.10.49 : I have a real problem; Christ called me to go out on the foreign missions; any sacrifice is worth that. But I cant stand all this craw-trumping, nit-picking about virtuous actions, the spiritual life, perfection, so many ejaculations a day, as if it was some kind a private game. God did not make us angels; he made us human; he doesn't keep a ledger of good and bad acts; he sees the heart. The Lord didn't forbid his disciples to speak to those they met on the road; he didn't say that women are a source of temptation, an occasion of sin. Some things are great here; some make me puke; we cant pick and choose. Almost two months gone and I haven't even thought of a cigarette. We are reading St. Luke's Gospel; I'd like to ask the Master about the eunuch; what did Jesus mean? No point in asking.

12.10.49 : Still haven't heard who won the All-Ireland. The spikey bracelets are not ornaments either. We make them ourselves from tough wire, just to keep our hands busy during recreation; also the scourge of cords, and the huge 15-decade rosary-beads that hang from the cincture. The Latin name for the bracelet is cilice; the big one goes on the thigh, the smaller one around the forearm, spikes turned in of course; worn twice a week till breakfast-time. They do bite a bit and cause some discomfort and swelling but are a joke; nothing compared to a pebble in your shoe. Now the old Irish monks were not joking; that was real penance - rolling in nettles and briars in their bare buff, and in snow too, when they could get it. Mrs Finn has been explaining about the clausura, the enclosure or cloister, the area of the monastery reserved by canon law for men only. The penalty for bringing in non-males would be excommunication reserved to the Pope, a most serious matter. The clausura is not so much for keeping us in as for keeping the women out; there's an unholy dread of the female species here; women are bad news; they would create havoc if they got at us. I sometimes wonder are the youths here all bachelors born only me?

25.10.49 : We have a bald monk from Waterford in the community; they say he's a mighty preacher; puts the fear of God in the hardened sinners who barely manage to make their Easter duty, known facetiously among the brethren here as 'the paschal rams'.. For relaxation in between his missions, he cuts down trees with an axe, like Gladstone. By the way, these long mounds of sand and gravel are called eskers and were left by the retreating glaciers of the last ice age. We were walking in solemn silence beyond the far esker in the early dusk, listening to Fr. Frank's axe ringing among the trees. We came on him; he was stripped to the waist; the chips were flying. Just then a shot rang out in the woods nearby. With his axe poised in mid-air and bald head glistening, the woodsman said out loud, to no one in particular, "Ah me, another inmate attempting to escape". How would we survive without a sense of humour?

31.10.49 : A very different Hollontide from this time twelve-month. No fun here. It's a cushy job, if you're built that way. In this all-male club I miss women's voivces; even old mad Trassa goldering across the lough would be heavenly music here .... Got another gunk; I may not get out on the foreign missions after all. The Master was withering, "You go where you're sent" ..... On top of all that I hear that you are sick, Bessy. I dont even know if it's serious and I cant write. Mother's letter merely said, "Besy's not well lately". I often think of you, the girl I left behind. All I can do is pray that you will be well again soon. Would you have taken me if I had asked you? We'll never know now.

24.11.49 : We are now allowed to attend Sunday Mass in the tribune of the public church, without being seen of course. One novice disappeared last week; never again mentioned. The Master reminds us, "Lose your vocation, lose your soul". The missioners are all away so Fr. Mike was called out of retirement again to preach; he has one string to his bow, coming late to Mass. He started off, "His lordship the bishop has laid down that I speak to you today on the subject of tradition. You have a tradition here of coming late to Mass", and he was off again on his hobbyhorse.

15.12.49 : In my mind's eye I can see our kitchen this minute; the girls dolling themselves up to the nines for the hop in the hall, laughing, shoving, all trying to see into the one looking-glass. The card-players are gathering in, slagging the young ones, setting them up with old bachelors with one foot in the grave, "He should be saying his prayers". Ma is settling down with her library book as the hubbub subsides. I remember a night; the wag of the card-school was early and she was telling him that her grandchild had ruined her beads that she got from Lourdes, "Pulled them asunder; what would have happened him if he had swallowed them?", she wondered. "Saving your presence, mam, he would have shit a decade".

20.12.49 : The monastery is a totally self-contained, self-sufficient community. The farm provides the food; the missions pay for the upkeep. Now that all the monks are home for Christmas, there must be well over a hundred men here under the one roof. The hours of the day are spelled out by the bell; the night is ruled by the great silence; not one word ever spoken except in extremis. The lay-brothers run the place like clockwork, Bro Cook, Bro Baker, Bro Farmer, Bro Tailor, Bro Porter, Bro Infirmarian, Bro Sacristan, Bro Hugh the Cobbler who builds the hugh-boots. Some of the older brothers cant read or write. Some are here sixty years and more; never got home since they entered. They do it for the Cross of Christ .... Bessy, I hear you're in the hospital, and I cant let on.

27.12.49 : First Christmas away from home. How I miss home and our gang; and I worry about you, Bessy, not knowing whether you're sick or well; no way to ask .... We had a party Christmas night and the novices were allowed to mingle with the community. Found out from a Corkman that Meath beat Cavan in the Football Final back in September .... Mutt and Jeff got into a chat with three ancient Limerick monks with sticks called Tom and Gerry and Mike, real playboys. Tom said, "Come on, Gerry, tell these two young whipper-snappers how Mike got his name". Gerry obliged, "The mornin Mike was christened his oul fella was drunk. The priest ast him what name he was callin the boy. Do you know what you'll do, Father", sez he,"you can call him Mike after Brian Boru".

31.12.49 : The last day of the Forties. Mrs Finn packed us off on a long country trudge to work off the heavy feeding. We came in sight of the town and the capo announced a five minute rest. I sat a little way off by myself on a stone wall. A huge orange sun slid quickly down over the rim of the flat land and dusk closed in. A gusty wisp of a breeze blew a clutch of finches over the wall. They swept round in a tight arc and settled as one on a clump of thistles, twittering, pecking the seeds. An old song I once heard floated back to me, 'Low lie the fields of Athenry, where once we saw the small free birds fly'. If I walked away right now, soon I'd reach the Shannon. I'd surely get a lift and be across the Erne by daylight. Dad had said the door was always open. A second gust swept the finches away and with them the wild, mad thought of freedom. The capo called time; the troops lined up; Jeff fell into step beside Mutt.

15.1.50 : It is peculiar how addicted to the potato the Irish are; any day an Irishman doesn't get his spuds, he thinks he's starving. No shortage of potatoes here; what I crave is some-thing decent to read. I got my hands on Allyson Peers' Life of Teresa of Avila; I was in clover till the Master saw it, "Too stim-ulating", says Mrs Finn. I'm not the pious type; saints working miracles by the new time is not my cup of tea. It's a lowering winter's evening, forlorn; white snow on black bog; the lowest point yet. Wandered aimlessly into the dust-room to polish my shoes for something to do, and bumped into a priest coming out in a hurry. What's this? In his haste he had left a book behind him. My heart gave a jump; the Irish Theological Quarterly, not exactly a spell-binder, but anything would be an improvement on St Simon Stylite cocked up on his roost and such wonders. With any luck I'd get a decko inside, before the next shoe-shin-er came. That first page changed my life forever. When the bell called, I was still engrossed, my foot up on the bench, the brush poised in my left hand. I stuffed the ITQ down behind the dust-bins; I'll be shining my shoes a lot for a while.

That first article is a savage attack on the new theologians, and I didn't even know until now that there were any new the-ologians. It seems the three ringleaders are Henri de Lubac, Yves Congar and Teilhard de Chardin. The gist of the article is that these men are dangerous; they are the modern modernists, out to destroy the church. They are preaching heresy; that the church is not static but dynamic, that it is evolving. They want to get rid of Latin and change the Mass, just like Luther. Where would that leave the teachings of the council of Trent? It hit me like a thunder-clap; these men are right. There must be change. From that moment, instead of looking back regretfully at the sacrifice I have made, I'm looking forward to the hope of great and exciting things to come .... Thank God you're feeling better, Bessy.... I couldn't sleep with all the jumble of thoughts; the lift-ing of the dark cloud of repression and fear; Newman's second spring; freedom of spirit; God's face not angry but kind; the Incarnation and Jesus and Mary; the parables. God is just but he is merciful too; fair play is the name of the game. Under the cler-ical barnacles is still the barque of Peter.

18.1.50 : I'll have to watch it or Mrs Finn will start asking why I'm polishing my shoes so often lately. Finding out about the new theology has changed everything; like a dark cloud lifting. This is actually old theology, as in St. Luke's gospel, the spirit and mind of Jesus telling us about the Father's heart, how it is kinder than any human father's ... 'If a child asks his father for bread, will he give him a stone?'. Jesus calls his father 'Abba, Daddy' .... Home and memories and you, Bessy, are still precious, but I have something to live for now, something I can love with all my heart. Even you I can give up gladly for this; all the pain of it is now worthwhile, to be a priest in a church where love casts out fear. I live for the day when I can find out more about de Lubac & co .... It's the system; the sadness of it, that the people fear the priest, while under the facade the priest is just another human being, with faults and failings like themselves .... Fr. Mike preached again last Sunday. He started off, "Four things the wise man could not understand, the way of the eagle through the skies, the way of the ship in mid-ocean, the way of the snake over the rock, and the way of a woman's heart". He pulled up his sleeves, "Now I'm going to explain them to you". The people stared up mutely at him; his two cronies chuckled in the tribune .... At the end of her letter Ma said, "Bessy is gone to England".

3.2.50 : We have the good and the bad here, the best and the worst. It's a great pity that the only way they know is putting us down; mocking; sneering. I know it's purpose is to test us; to teach humility. But surely honey is better than vinegar any day. All this suppression of human feelings and they come out anyway in other forms. As it happens, I have poor eyesight but can hear the grass growing. We have a stable of old war-horses here, now retired with the shoes off and out at grass. In their day they terrorised the country with their rip-roaring sermons on hell-fire. A group of them were doddering along the far esker. We all heard the loud guffaw; my sharp ears picked up the joke, "Mike says he's not going to say the office any more, because, when King David couldn't throw his leg over a woman any more, he sat down and wrote the psalms". These old codgers sure are human.

49

15.3.50 : Not much happening; the same routine day in day out. Day thoughts have dried up; my mind is a blank. But they still run riot at night. Bessy's gone; did I love her? Anyway, I went my way and now she's gone hers .... The other day three of us were sent round to weed the front garden. A window was slightly open at the bottom and we could catch snippets of the news on the wireless. Dr. Noel Browne, the minister of health, is at loggerheads with the bishops over the mother-and-child scheme. If you ask me, Browne is doing a helluva lot more for the poor than the bishops are. He's a brave man to take them on; once they start this communist hare, he's a dead duck .... At chapter each day we have to kneel and accuse ourselves of our faults. One poor innocent soul said he had a bit of fluff under his bed. Jeff thought that funny but the faces all along the circle were as solemn as judges ... It seems the nuns indulge in the discipline too. Imagine the dainty ladies letting down their bloomers and whacking away, and their pink bottoms turning red in the sunset. Naughty, naughty, Jeff; down boy, down .... But seriously, this is barbaric. Whatever about us haverils, girls should not have to undergo this outrageous indignity. If decent people only knew. Better days ahead, please God .... The zealator, one of our own maryah but a Trojan horse, inspects our cells, for bits of fluff and such. I worry about him finding my book of numbers. Why do I take the risk? I read of a man who survived four years of the Nazi concentration camps by writing his secret thoughts and dreams on scraps of paper. Helped him to survive. So by me.

1.4.50 : Some of this piety is a bit gushy for me; Mrs Finn says Jeff is a cold fish. For sure I dont wear my heart on my sleeve. Some of them are getting a bit carried away with their fervour; tell-tale red spots on the wall where somebody drew blood. Mrs Finn issued a warning to go easy on the bum and sent me to wash the wall. I'm not one of his favourites. Surely they dont have to sqeeze the humanity out of us like an orange, to make us tough soldiers of Christ. When the Master (alias Mrs. Finn) beckons ominously and I follow him into the office for our weekly tete-a-tete, my heart drops into my boots. I have little to say. He probes, trying to draw me out. I sing dumb, knowing what he's at. They want to wipe the slate clean; start off with a complete tabula rasa; make us over into their own image of clerical yes-men. Not me. I have tasted the new wine; God wants us to be more, not less human .... We meditate for half-an-hour three times a day on our knees. In the early morning the reader's voice drones on, the reading as dry as dust, about the virtues, as if they were in pidgeon-holes in God's post-office. My mind goes back to the sunshine on the big lough and the fish rising and all the world awash in birdsong. I look out at the dreary, flat bog and in my mind I see a high bog aflame in purple heather, and a boy running barefoot in the squelching moss, picking the bog-cotton and the raspberries. Bitter-sweet memories; I can never go back. No matter. The foreign missions beckon far away, to tell the people the good news about the son of God who called himself the son of man. You pays your price and you takes your choice. We are the privileged few. We escape the heart-aches that flesh is heir to, the hardships and worries, the struggles of the rest of humanity. But we pay in loneliness. This is the golden opportunity to be a saint, or to be as selfish as be-damned. The old Greeks had a thing they called hubris, the stuff of tragedy; the pride of refusing to be human; tempting the gods; sticking one's neck out. My heart aches for a soul-mate; this is the price. My companions seem as serene as angels; who knows what goes on in the depths, perhaps unknown even to themselves ..... We have fasting during lent, one square meal and two collations of two ounces each, and black coffee; no meat except on Sundays; stomachs growl and rumble in the dark chapel, and bring the souls lost in contemplation or in slumber back down to earth, with a snort here and a titter there. Horses can sleep standing up; some soon get the hang of sleeping on elbows and knees without moving a muscle.

Chapter 5

Easter Mon. 1950 : All the missioners are home for Easter. They were strolling along the far esker after the dinner yesterday in twos and threes, swapping accounts of their exploits around the country. They gathered round to listen to Fr. Bullyboy, boasting of his latest coup de main, "Johnny here was preaching and I took a stroll around the village, just on the off-chance that somebody might be ducking the mission. Out of the corner of my eye I caught a movement. A curtain fell back into place. 'Ha ha, me hearty', sez I. I walked in and there she was, a big, strapping lump of a lassy skulking behind the curtain, but the bulge of her rump was showing. She made a dash to cut out by me like a skittish heifer, but I was too quick for her. I got a couple of sweet skelps across the buttocks at her that put a spring in her step up the street and me after her. She made the chapel in jig-time with me right behind her, chivvying her on to her duty, ha ha ha". They thought it was hilarious. What wit; what humour. Please God, there are better days ahead.

9.5.50 : Mrs Finn dropped a bombshell today. Out of the blue he remarks casually that PJ Duke is dead. My idol gone at 26; buried in Stradone yesterday. I had a hard time holding back the tears; the Master spotted it; he has a soft spot in him somewhere. He walked out and was back in a thrice with a football in his hands, "Let's see whether any of this bunch of bowzies can kick football".

10.5.50 : How did I survive without football for nearly nine months? I was in ecstasy, in the seventh heaven, racing like a colt let out after months in winter dark, on the lovely sandy springy sod between the eskers. Nothing will ever compare with that magic half-hour, floating on air, the ball on a string, the old monks pausing to watch. And all the while I heard the ringing voice painting the magic picture from the Polo Grounds, the surging solo-run, the red head flaring in the battle's thrill. So I mourned the passing of my hero.

15.5.50 : Yesterday I took a chance. We had a whole hour free, each one on his own, strolling around the grounds in silence. When no one was looking I ducked into the woods and followed the path, just to see what I might see. Soon I came to the edge of the trees. A short distance out in the bog a man was cutting turf by himself, a tedious process. From cover I watched him for a while, as he patiently laid the sods up on the bank, climbed out and placed them one by one on the barrow, wheeled them out and heeled them, then cut another load. He became aware of my presence and glanced over and I ventured out. While he worked we talked quietly about the weather and the crops, and compared this shallow bog with ours back home. He knew I was out of bounds but passed no remarks. A lark warbled straight overhead and we listened to her in silence until she dropped the last fifty feet like a stone into her nest. "It's hard on your own", I said. The wife has consumption; only for Noel Browne she'd be dead, God spare him. We parted,"Say a prayer for Maggy, Brother". I nodded, "Mum's the word", and he nodded back, understanding. I left him laying the shiny brown slabs on the bank. One by one the fresh sods turned colour through all the shades from brown-red to jet black.

20.5.50 : At home Dad would be cutting turf these days too. Lying awake in the night, I can see the shiny wet slabs coming up like clockwork off the slane, and the clock in the church tower tolls the time. I can see the river-bank carpeted with wildflowers; the air is alive with bees and birdsong and the calls of loughfowl and many corncrakes and far and near cuckoos. The past slips away. I say over and over the names of the prophets of a better tomorrow, Yves Congar, Henri de Lubac, Teilhard de Chardin, Berhard Haring. In the daily chapter of faults we kneel and accuse ourselves of breaches of the holy rule and having a bit of fluff under the bed. In the drowsy afternoon the voice drones on, reading the lives of the saints, "The monk Simeon practised thirteen separate acts of mortification in eating a boiled egg" .... This is the jubilee year; we got this custom from the Jews, God's chosen people; every fifty years it was a time of turning back to God, forgiving and asking forgiveness, cancelling debts, giving slaves their freedom; handing back alienated lands to the original owners. It was so-called because the start of this time was heralded by the blowing of a ram's horn. What a pity the practical aspects have been lost; all that is left now is the dubious idea of indulgences and some empty fanfare, for which ' media hype' is the latest American coinage.

7.6.50 : Today I escaped again. The turfman was footing but he had help; Maggy was back, the two bending, heads close in quiet words, rising together to stretch aching backs. The hen lark was coming down the long stairs of heaven above them, fluttering on her wings of song. I let them be, not wishing to break the spell. Footing turf with my girl did not bear thinking of ..... Mrs Finn warned us of the danger of particular friendships, without spelling out what exactly the danger was. Also the rule of touch; it is very strictly forbidden to touch another person, for any reason. The silence here is precious; I like my own company in solitude; here God walks in the garden. They tell us He asks this sacrifice but my heart isn't in it.

29.6.50 : Some of the old brothers can't read or write. Bro Dominic has been here since 1900; never went home. He has spent his life from the age of 16 in a house of preachers and teachers, tripping over books at every turn. He can't read a newspaper and is not allowed to listen to the wireless. It doesn't add up in my book .... We went to the seaside for the day last Thursday; swam at Salthill; visited the church in Spiddal to see the stain-glass windows; very beautiful. I was down; heart in boots; don't know why; Mrs Finn twigged it, I could see. I think I'm a kind of an enigma to him as well as myself. We visited Pearse's cottage in Rosmuck; it made me more down; all the young men, Catholic, Protestant and Dissenter, made cannon-fodder, in the Somme and Sackville Street and at El Alamein, and for what? all the lovely young flowers of the forest gone, only to make a bad job worse .... The swimming-pool is still only a hole in the ground; it raised many a blister on the tender hands of the townies, until they developed calluses like us farmers. The next generation will have to finish the job, good luck to them.

15.7.50 : Fr. Mel was like a walking ghost, as thin as a rail, with long flowing white hair. He glided among the laurels of the far esker, as if his feet didn't touch the ground. It was a pity of him; they say his mind snapped just after his ordination more than 20 yrs ago. He spoke to no one and had never gone outside the enclosure. We were deep in meditation last Tuesday morning when a stir at the door brought us back from the heights of contemplation or the depths of slumber, as the case might be. Mrs Finn rapped on the pew and said that Fr. Mel was missing. He sent us, two by two, out through the countryside to look for him. Joxer and I took the bog route. After slogging through the spongy moss and hip-high heather for maybe an hour, we came to the railway line, and sat down on the embankment for a rest. We heard a rumble like distant thunder, the Dublin train coming. Gradually the sound got louder; the whistle blew for a level crossing, and like a little shiny caterpiller far away, she came slowly round the long curve, the sunlight glinting on the windows. Far ahead the wraithlike figure of Fr. Mel flitted, hopping the sleepers in his bare buff. We watched, spellbound, as the gap closed rapidly. Then the whistle screamed and he veered off into the sallies. The poor man was found later in the morning, face down in a boghole. We buried him yesterday. His poor tortured soul has found peace at last.

1.8.50 : Bad thoughts are no joke here; very serious. I had another bad dream last night. Reminds me of the man going to confession and the priest asked him if he was troubled with bad thoughts. "Ara not a bit o' trouble atall, Fr." Where I come from, such thoughts are only natural; it's what you do about them that counts. One cant let them run amuck of course; still I don't agree with burying them either. In the dream we were coming out of the Ulster Final in Clones and I got crushed up against a big buxom lassy decked out in the Antrim colours. It wasn't my fault but I enjoyed it anyway, God forgive me. Mrs. Finn hasn't mentioned wet dreams.

24.8.50 : The big day is Sept. 8; the long retreat begins tonight; no talking at all to anyone for 15 days. The fervour is starting to gush all round me; maybe I am a cold fish, but I can't get worked up. This can't last; I wonder what happens when the veneer of piety wears off. I'm game for this life and I'll give it my best shot, but I can't get carried away. Now if it was a football match, or a cockfight, or a hunt, it would be a different story. A horrible thought just hit me; could some be joining up for the cushy ride? I hear tell of some and it's the mother has the vocation. I went to confession to one of the missioners. His cell was as neat as a pin. No bit of fluff hiding under his bed. I should have been concentrating on my sins but I couldn't help counting; he had his 20 pairs of shoes lined up like soldiers. Now I ask you. Da has his hobnails and the one pair of Sunday-shoes he bought in Lisnaskea before the war .... Mrs Finn said the Holy Father was bringing out a new encyclical condemning the new theology. Sometimes in the night the thought crosses my mind, "What in God's name am I doing here?". And yet I have this unwavering sense of being called. I live in hope. The church Christ founded in not a one-man band; The new theology will win out in time, with the help of God. In a fortnight's time we will be taking the three vows of poverty, chastity and obedience. There was a time when the priests were not all monks. Was St. Patrick a monk?

3.9.50 : The vow of poverty; Christ has many things to say about the poor and being poor in spirit, that is, living detached from the love of money and material things. Not only monks, all Christians must choose between God and Mammon. Am I poor now? Will I ever want for anything as a priest? Here am I in the lap of luxury and my brothers and sisters have to go to England and Canada to make a living. Who's codding who? Here we have it made for life; never a care where the next square meal is coming from. Every man-jack of us has put on weight since we came, 'like young bullocks in after-grass' the Master says. We do need this new theology, to get back to the poor man of Nazareth, who had not a place to lay his head .... We come next to chastity, self-control. Every Christian, married and single, is called to live a chaste life. This vow is more, celibacy, a solemn promise not to marry. It makes sense for us monks, especially those who go on the missions. Long ago the secular priests were free to marry, as they still are in the eastern church. St. Peter was married and Christ cured his mother-in-law. Anyway, regardless of what I think, this is now the narrow gate to the priesthood. I enter willingly, praying for the grace to be faithful, but in all honesty, the prospect has no natural attraction. With God's help I'll be faithful .... Mrs Finn lays great stress on the vow of obedience. Pride has to be eradicated, root and branch, before any virtue will grow in the garden of the soul. The monk must give blind obedience to his superior; he must be prepared, at a moment's notice, to go anywhere at his bidding, no matter what he himself thinks. The voice of the superior is the voice of God, the monastery bell tolling for the daily exercises is the symbol, the constant reminder. He must give true interior assent. What about his conscience? The good monk can rest assured that his superior knows best and will not order him to commit sin. I have a problem with this blind obedience, it seems to me to short-circuit faith in God. When I brought this up the Master seemed to take the attitude that I was trying to be a smart aleck and I didn't press it. What I find hard is that we are not really free to question the status quo; who wants to be marked out as a trouble-maker? I happen to know that it was Ignatius Loyola who introduced this concept of blind obedience, because he had been an army officer and was used to having the power of life and death over his men. You wont find this mentality in Christ; he invited people to follow him freely, using moral persuasion. He went to great pains to instruct the apostles specifically not to imitate the great ones of this world on this very point; "those who lord it over their subjects; it must not be so with you". As he says, it is the spirit, not the letter, that counts. And the apostles got the message; when it came to the rub and their lives were on the line, they said they had to obey God rather than men. I never cared for Loyola no more than Augustine, intellectual snobs both of them; they perverted the teaching of Jesus; they both lack the milk of human kindness. Teresa, now there's a human being for you; a great woman and a great saint .... The Good Samaritan didn't know about the rule of touch.

8.9.50 : Dad and Mam came for the big day yesterday; what a happy time we had. Mother, her face beaming as if she was already in heaven, sat among the old monks, swopping stories and pinches of snuff. Before he left Dad said again, "Remember, the door is always open". What the neighbours might say wouldn't bother him. I'm lucky in my parents compared to most, who are put in the minor seminary by the mother while they are still children. Over the first hurdle; tomorrow we head for the city and the house of studies. 19 of us have survived. Mrs. Finn and the leprachaun and the bedford will take us to the train, wearing our clerical collars and hats for the first time, and our chesterfield coats down to our knees, the handiwork of Bro Tailor & Co. The Master gave us our last pep-talk before facing the big, bad world, "No talking to strangers on the train; modesty of the eyes, especially where females of the opposite species are concerned; the eyes are the windows of the soul". I will miss the solitude of this holy place, where God managed somehow to get a few hometruths through my thick skull.

15.9.50 : The sem a colossal, hectic place; eighty-five students; counting priests and lay-brothers, more than 150 all told. Stagefright after all the months in the bog-solitude. Each one of us has an angel-guardian to show us the ropes. Football twice a week. All sorts of jobs, bee-keeping. printing, book-binding, gardening, building, electricity. I was lucky to get someting I like, a job in the carpenter's shop. A list appeared on the noticeboard this morning, giving the names of those picked to go to the University. The Kerryman and I are down for Latin and Greek; not bad, but a pity it wasn't Irish and English. Three miles to the uni, twice a day on bicycles, rain or shine. We are not to speak to anyone, even the other students in class, except about studies. Outside the sem we may talk to one another only in Irish. The word is that any slips get back to the sem before we do; don't know who the stool-pidgeon is yet. The first chance, I got my hands on de Lubac. This is the stuff. They invited him to Rome for a grilling but the word got out. T de Chardin died last year, all alone in New York, a broken man, his life's work comdemned by the Vatican. It's Luther and Bellarmine all over again; stirring times. Our boss here is JJ; he has a watery eye and a poor opinion of human nature and belongs to the old school. Strong on the don'ts; wouldn't see eye-to-eye with the new theology. I'll have to be careful and keep my mind to myself; the blinds are down, Joxer, the blinds are down. The Pope has come out with an encyclical against the new theology. He has no time for the dynamic view of the church, which is strange, for he is a dynamic and brilliant man in many ways; but he's a one-man band. It's a pity that he has to do everything himself without consulting the bishops.

10.10.50 : Uni is exciting but it's hard not talking to anyone. Saw a couple of people from home I recognised but kept going. They must think it odd. We can't join in any games or activities, can't watch games or listen to games on the wireless. Only us two in the Greek class; Mutt and Jeff. We have a monk-professor with a bog-accent who teaches sociology. He takes on him to be the bishops' mouthpiece; Noel Browne has to be taught a lesson; who runs this country anyway, the Catholic bishops or the politicians? Dr. Browne is a socialist, a communist and an anticlerical. The betting is heavy that Phely won't open the sociology textbook that he's paid to teach, this side of Hollontide. We can't read the newspaper or listen to the wireless but are gradually picking up the gist of what has been happening while we were hibernating out in the bog. A coalition of Fine Gael and the Clan have ousted Dev and the boys, and have made the Free State a republic. What's this we hear? Sean McBride is turning our holy Catholic Ireland, which God sent Dev and JC McQuaid to enshrine in the constitution, into a godless state. In the election campaign they put Dev up on a white horse in Ennis. Two Clare farmers were arguing, "Pat, willya look at the oul eejit up on the horse"; "You're wrong there, Mick", "What do you mean?"; "That's not a horse, it's a mare". At the Uni a Corkman with a walrus mustache is our professor of English. He talks about anything under the sun only English; yesterday spent 50 mins explaining how they got a knight in full armour up on his horse back in the middle ages. They say his chair was a political plum, that he has no degree in anything, "Are oo from Cark,

59

bye?". Kate is our professor of Irish; she talks perfect dialect, so perfect that no one can get a word she says. The fior-gaels are the bane of our lives; it's not real Irish with the blas unless you put a couple of pebbles under your uvula and drag up phlegm.

1.11.50 : Fr. Stan visited from Belfast and was telling us about the mission to non-Catholics every year during lent. Many ministers of the different denominations attend. The highlight each evening is a tour of church and monastery, explaining the history of vestments, holy water, the sacraments, chalice, incense etc. Much interest. Only one clergyman so far struck Fr. Stan as a bad egg, "His name is the Rev Ian Paisley; full of hatred of all things Catholic; he's no man of God; I don't know why he came" .... Fr. Phely, our friar defender of the faith at the uni, hasn't opened the book yet; still too busy lambasting Dr. Browne and his mother-and-child scheme, which violates Catholic ethical principles. Dad's pet peeve was that Rome had no problem violating Catholic ethical principles of justice and fair play in the matter of mixed marriages. " The birds will come home to roost, every last one of them", was his refrain. Dad is no bigot; he calls a spade a spade, whatever it's colour; he just cant stand hypocrisy from people who claim a monopoly of virtue.

17.11.50 : Mutt and Jeff make up the whole Greek class at the Uni. Rev Professor Tom is tired of the long losing battle to revive dead Greek; he'd much rather be facing a stone wall on his big hunter with the Galway Blazers. The same identical ritual is repeated every morning among the dusty tomes, "What are we doing? Thucydides, is that so? Which book? Where did we stop?". We translate, turn and turn about, the Peloponnesian war, the seige of Syracuse, and Tom dozes. Mutt hasn't a long head on him for nothing; he can read Greek like Ireland's Own or The Kerryman. Mutt and Jeff are good friends; not particular friends mind you, that's forbidden by the holy rule and they're not built that way anyway. Though friends, their minds are poles apart. Mutt is a born monk; wouldn't even look twice at a woman; Jeff has no objection to the female species at all. They both sail a little close to the wind but for very different reasons. Mutt is determined to avoid a teaching career and to get out on the foreign missions, so he's not going to shine at the books; he'll just do enough to get by, a tricky maneuvre. Jeff's danger is his penchant for the new theology. Jeff dresses dapper, even in canonicals. Not Mutt. Under a long bedraggled raincoat, and a slouch hat somewhere between black and green, and a mighty pair of brogues, winter and summer he wears nothing next his skin, no underwear, no socks, only an old Kerry jersey, and a set of cast-iron trousers that can stand up by themselves. Some pair these two, the long and the short of it, tearing down Bothermore and across Eyre Square, sailing over the Salmonweir Bridge and round by the Gaol, black coat-tails flying, in the year of Our Lord, 1950.

13.1.51 : Hurrah! We are allowed to listen to the wireless for half an hour every Sunday, to hear Alisdair Cooke's Letter from America .... Hurrah and Haliluia! Fr. Pat has come back from Rome to teach us theology, half-year there, half-year here. He is bubbling over with the very latest happening in the world of the new theology. He knows many of these men personally. The hackles of the old guard are up, but Pat rattles away merrily in the lilting Kerry accent; he's not afraid of bogiemen. His class is pure joy, Newman's second spring is dawning in the church; great changes coming in the wind. The old guard send up their champion, James, an old war-horse, a power in his day who dominated lesser minds, cowed them with caustc wit. It's David versus Goliath all over again, the dynamic taking on the static. Pat knows his stuff; James relies on his reputation; he hasn't read a book in 20 yrs. Battle is joined, war to the death for the minds and hearts of the monks. Jeff is not on his own any more, but still plays his cards close to his chest; you could still disappear in the night if you got tagged as a liberal. There is so much to read in the college library, Graham Greene, Belloc, Chesterton, Waugh. Just discovered Steinbeck, Cannery Row, The Grapes of Wrath, Of Mice and Men. Am beginning to realise that this is a privileged life. I'm a hero in my brothers' and sisters' eyes; their lot is harder than mine. It's easy to love our brothers as long as we can keep them at arm's length, and our sisters on the other side of the clausura.

2.2.51 : Fr. Pat was invited to give a talk at the Uni last night. The aula maxima was packed. He had them in the hollow of his hand with his vision of the church of tomorrow; reform must come; love of God and neighbour is the basic principle of the Christian life, as Christ said, not fear and coercion and control. He talked about the heresy of Jansenism and the terrible damage it had done to the church and to people's lives. He told how Jansenism, which makes God out to be a fear-inspiring taskmaster, rather than a loving father, had infected and poisoned the Irish church. Maynooth was dangled by the British in front of the bishops, as a bribe to buy them off against the United Irishmen. The first professors in Maynooth, imported by the bishops from France, were Jansenists. Every priest ever taught in Maynooth has been infected with the disease, passed on from generation to generation. Then he spoke of the new spirit on the continent, back to the New Testament and the words and actions of Jesus. The second spring, foretold by Newman, was coming, "Lift up your hearts" .... First thing this morning, a big wagon of a motor-car purred up to the front door of the sem. The driver got out and handed in a letter, from his lordship. His Jansenist nose is out of joint; Fr. Pat's lecture is not to his liking. This cleric is silenced forthwith, forbidden to speak in public again in his diocese. Signed Michael of Galway. We are all stunned, all except Fr. Pat himself; he chuckles in high glee, "Case in point, case in point". These are surely stirring times to be a seminarian and twenty-one.

6.3.51 : Fr. Pat was telling us about the priest-workers in France; they are doing wonderful work in the factories, among the working-class and the poor; but Rome frowns. It is really up to the bishops to take a stand. "They are bullied by Rome; the Irish bishops are bullied by John Charles in Dublin and Michael Browne here in Galway". He goes on to talk to us about the college of bishops .... Another sign of the times; there is talk of elections in the order for the first time ever; until now the same safe men have been appointed by Rome and rotated around the different monasteries. Things would change overnight if we could choose our own superiors, rather than having Rome's choice imposed on us. But will they trust us that far? .... We have some heated debates on politics; Dev has his devotees but he is not everyone's favourite. The wag said that Dev would have made a good monk; a holy man; look at his face, he even looks like Pope Pius X11. He comes to visit us here whenever he's down this way. Some of the old monks do him homage; others are not so reverent, going so far as to cast doubt on his parentage. Bro Cutty was overheard muttering, 'the long spanner get'.

'' 27.3.51 : The priest in charge of the young lay-brothers has a mighty girth and so is known as Friar Tuck; he has the cut of a substantial bishop about him; the wag says he suffers from a condition known as suppressed episcopacy. He takes out his frustration on the poor brothers. We take turns helping with the wash-up. The other evening we were all pitching in in the kitchen, all chatter and banter, when Tuck hove in sight, sailing along on an even keel like a laden galleon. It seems one of the brothers had committed some heinous crime or other, and the great one took the opportunity for a public humiliation.. The merry chatter died like birdsong in a thunderstorm; "Down on your knees', he commanded and he laced into him. The poor boy tried to say something in his own defence, only to bring on a worse tirade. When he had finished his harangue he sailed out, leaving the brother on his knees. Stunned silence; then old Brother Cutty said, "Darest thou to answer the high-priest so?" .... The story goes that another brother, after the war, came back from the Philippines, where he had been kept in solitary confinement by the Japanese, under a harsh Korean jailor. He was still a bit stir-crazy, as the Americans call it. The claustraphobia of the monastery was very hard on him. It was a lovely day so he asked his boss, the same Friar Tuck, for permission to go out for a walk and a swim. Permission refused. The brother watched his chance and slipped off. But Tuck had his eye on him. When the escapee reached Salthill, there was his gaoler waiting for him. Tuck had taken the bus. And he went back on the bus and the brother walked. The poor man did a few more days in solitary. He said the Korean couldn't hold a candle to Tuck in the cruelty stakes. The Korean was doing it because otherwise he'd get it in the neck himself from the Japs; Tuck was doing it out of the fulness of a bitter heart.

3.4.51 : Our days are full. We play football on Sundays and soccer on Tuesdays, prayers, study, carpenter's shop; not enough hours in the day. Canon Hines, the PP in Salthill, is famous for his spoonerisms. He was going out to play golf and left a stamped, addressed letter on the hall-stand, reminding both the housekeeper and the maid to give it to the postman. When he returned it was still sitting where he had left it and he shouted in to the kitchen, "Which of yez pissed the most?" He was recounting how the bishop shanked his tee-shot and hit a sheep, "His Lordship went in the rough and shit a heap" ..... Christy Ring is still poetry in motion; mighty tussles with Tommy Doyle; we get the matches blow by blow through the grapevine.

30.4.51 : This regime, in spite of all the don'ts and repression, is still full of marvellous opportunities; true freedom is in the mind, if one keeps the mind open. Most of the monks are decent men, some even warm human beings; though the products of an inherently defective system. But it's hard to excuse them for not wanting to change things which cannot sit well with any sane conscience. It's their safety-first attitude that galls me; very few want to take a risk; they like their comfort.. In this terrible negative attitude to women, I am convinced that training and education has left them that they know no better, God .help them. There is male and female in all of us, the balance tilted ever so slightly one way or the other, dominant or recessive. You can see we are studying Mendelsohn, and sometimes my mind goes haywire. If they only knew what goes on behind the placid smile. Augustine ruined the church; his legacy lives with us to this day. Underpinning everything is the blind, unthinking fear of woman as the temptress who drags man down with her into original sin. Blame everything on her. The irony is that, in striving to root out all female contamination, the regime produces emasculated males, who cannot relate to women on the one hand, and only feebly to men on the other. Some essential human ingredient is lost in the process. When a hen starts crowing in the farmyard, neither hens nor cocks like it and they

64

ostracise her. Add to this the very real danger of sexual carry-on in all-male company. The miracle is that so many of those who enter at 13 are half-way human at all, in spite of the regime. I had a long chat with Fr. Pat and he agrees with me, but warned me to keep my thoughts to myself or I wouldn't be ordained. These jottings are my way of getting things off my chest. It keeps me sane. I'm all right as long as I can see the humour of it.

1.7.51 : We are down here in Clifden for 5 wks, a glorious place. Ten of us finished at the Uni early and cycled the 60 odd miles by the coast road out through Spiddal and the Pearse country and Roundstone. Our jobs as carpenters, block-makers, etc, was to get the place in order after the long months with no heat in it and no caretaker since last August. With the big increase in numbers we had to renovate the stables as sleeping quarters. Mighty proud of the new refectory, built in 10 days; had windows and doors ready beforehand. We are on a peninsula jutting out into the Atlantic, with a deep bay with steep rocky sides like a fiord on either side, going far inland at high tide. O beautiful Connemara! a marvellous place, even in bad weather, which it is just now. In the evening a blanket of dense wet fog swirls in from the sea and soaks everything. The sheep lament like lost souls out in the mist and the curlews and sea-birds sound lonesome too. They say Lady Gregory and Yeats and their friends used to come here in summers long ago. The novelist Ethel Mannin still comes to a cottage nearby for the summer. We are not supposed to speak to anyone even here, and she is named specifically every year as a threat to holy youths, vowed to celibacy. I must make it my business to bump into her by accident. A tacit exception is made for Willy Mulkerns, the local man who brings the milk every morning. Willy is not regarded as a serious threat; poor Willy is harmless; he has a flow of rustic sayings as colourful as bunting at a fair; no plain, pedestrian patter from Willy, "Like the clappers o' hell; the two ends of a blackguard; let the hare sit; all her geese are swans". "Well, William, how's it goin the day?"- "Tearin away lek a tinker's shirt". Willy talks at the top of his voice, from having the words torn from his mouth all his life by the

Atlantic winds .... We have two big boats, deep, wide in the beam; the prospects are pleasing, I can see great times ahead, going out to the open sea and the islands. Some genius on high, who obliviously knows nothing about water, has decided in his almighty wisdom, that we cannot have engines, for safety reasons. Any fool could figure out that you are far safer if you have power on water, but no matter, with strong arms pulling four sweeps and two oars, we'll make the best of it; we'll go places. Weather wet; sea rough; we'll be out as soon as a lull comes. Our reading is censored but I got my hands on Brighton Rock. Obviously JJ hasn't read it, and presumes that it's safe because Graham Greene is a convert to Catholicism.

15.7.51 : Ten of us volunteered to sleep in a big army tent in the garden; it saw better days; leaks like a sieve; weather still bad. We moved to higher ground; put in floor-boards; still the water comes in and down and up. But nothing can get a man down in this wondrous place; some go fishing for trout; some cycle; some hike; some climb; some read. The wild wind has died and the boatmen head out to sea, come rain or shine. Half a mile across the bay a former generation christened the high rocks Biserte, and put a diving-board there, 30 foot above the water. Only the hardiest venture. The weather is settling into balmy summer and Joxer and his tennis buffs have the nets up and we hear the genteel sounds of racquet on ball. For the feeble there is miniature golf and croquet. Even here we have a clausura, not to keep us in but to keep females out. In canon law, to bring a woman inside the fence incurs excommunication, reserved to the Pope no less. The only females likely to break in here are stray sheep.

11.9.51 : Two years down and six to go. Back to the Uni. It's interesting to observe the passing scene and wonder have other people the same thoughts, the same feelings as I have. We are taught Plato's doctrine, courtesy of Augustine, that the holy soul in ensnared in the sinful body, like a bird in a cage. For me, my body, unruly though it be, is me as much as my soul is. I was reading about sublimation; if we supress feelings, like capping

66

a well, they break out in some other form, and do serious damage. The only convincing reason that I can see for making a sacrifice is for love. I am trying to grasp the real meaning of the cross; when the house is on fire, the furniture goes out the window. Surely our destiny is to follow in the footsteps of him who took a human body; we are meant, not to become angels but to become fully human, a true son of man.

5.10.51 : We have plays every Christmas in both English and Irish. I got a part in the English play, Shop at Slye Corner this year. I find it very hard to act here, to let myself go; I cant afford to let the real me be seen. I've a woman's part and that makes it so much the harder. It's frustrating. You know how I love acting, getting into the character, body and soul. They tell me I'm good, but I'm only a pale shadow of myself, an empty shell. I feel that if I threw myself into it they would see my soul, and that I can't afford. Do you remember when we did Juno?, so long ago now, and before that Iosagan, when we were children? .... Haliluia!, at long last we can listen once more to Micheal O'Hehir's magic voice bringing us the football. Cavan doing well.

15.1.52 : Fr Pat continues to bring back rousing news from the Continent. He has worked in parishes, mostly in France and Germany since last year. He was telling us about the Mass in Holland; it was in Dutch and the priest was facing the people. Just imagine, the way it was at the start in the Roman catacombs. Cardinal Ottaviani & co don't like it, he says, and are also thinking of suppressing the worker priests.

13.3.52 : There is still some justice in the world after all; a wet fairday in Galway; cattle filling the lower end of Bohermore and spilling down into Eyre Square, roads and sidewalks blocked, watery cow-skitter wall-to-wall; a precarious place on a bicycle. Four of us came down. A lump of a bull calf picked that moment to cross over; three steered round him. The bull calf changed his mind again and cut back; the fourth cyclist veered and skidded, then slid through the cow-dung on his back. As he gathered himself up he was still talking Irish. Fair dues to him; he's the pidgeon who carries the stories back to the boss..

Chapter 6

15.7.52 : Back in Clifden again. the big news is that they are making a picture up at Cong. It's called The Quiet Man, starring John Wayne and Maureen O'Hara and Barry Fitzgerald. We have been warned from on high not to go anywhere near the place, and the stool-pidgeon will be watching; but we have him spotted; that's half the battle; we'll best him. As Willy Mulkerns says, "A wink is as good as a nod to a blind horse". Willy informs us that the pony-racing sequences will be shot on Lettergesh strand. We'll approach from the sea, and bring the spy-glasses, fulfilling the letter, if not the spirit, of the law. W will keep us informed, mum's the word.

26.7.52 : The past 2 days have been fun, watching the mey-hem on Lettergesh strand. How they can turn this chaos into a movie sequence baffles imagination. With the glasses we had a grandstand view from the sand-dunes, the Duke strutting his stuff as if he had a ramrod up his behind, and Maureen O'Hara was easy to spot; her flaming hair could be seen for miles, even with the naked eye. Our own sequel was not so good. We were bested by the squeeler; JJ knew all about our escapade before we were halfway home. The spy must have had a bicycle and make good time, while we had to go the long way round by the water like Brian O'Lynn. We'll get him yet; he's attending the Uni with us, for if any of us kicks over the traces in the slight-est, JJ has it for us, chapter and verse. He doesn't know that we know who he is. For spying on the Quiet Man, the boat crew are condemned to wearing cilices three mornings and no swim-ming for a week. Not as bad as poor John of the Cross long ago, Mother Teresa's friend; his fellow-monks didn't like him show-ing them up as lax monks by his strictness, so they imprisoned him for months on bread and water, and used the good old dis-cipline on him twice a day. We haven't heard the end of it but are homing in on the stool-pidgeon .... The good news is that Cavan won the Ulster Final.

7.8.52 : When we got back from Clifden the whole sem was put on a day's retreat for all of Sunday, no talking, no football, no Micheal O'Hehir from Croke Park, everything but the sack-cloth and ashes. This is of course in punishment for the crimes of the holidays. JJ lectured us for well over an hour, on and on and on, discipline breaking down, no respect, flouting the holy rule, no interior life. At one point he was almost crying; in a way I felt sorry for him; things are changing and he cant cope. He keeps harping on the way things were in his day, totally seclud-ed from the world and happy in his vocation. All gone; no more modesty of the eyes; the rule of touch is ignored; the wonderful community spirit of the past is breaking up into cliques. Poor JJ is losing it. There are worse things going on that he doesn't seem to be aware of. He worries about the little, piddly Italian rules that turn men into automatons. He punishes the whole student body because a few of us looked at Maureen O'Hara's hair through binoculars, because his snitch ran to him with a tale of harmless horseplay. The touch of a human hand can mean many things. I came across dubious carry- on in the boarding-school, but hardly expected to find it here. From the first day I became aware that we have our share of the pansy type. That's as may be, and maybe that sort are considered by the powers-that-be to be good, safe material for the priesthood. I have my doubts. But pansies or not, they should mind their own business and keep their hands to themselves. Mark Twain's mother sent him out to weed the flower-bed; he want-ed to flower the weed-bed. Surely an oppressive regime should at least be able to uncover the bad eggs. We were out at the pier on Mannin Bay one day during the holidays. A rough-and-tumble game of rugby developed. I'm almost sure that was the incident reported back to JJ, that upset him so much. What I know and he doesn't, is that a big literary type got me down and held me down. It dawned on me that he was getting a dif-ferent kind of kick out of the tussle than I was. I applied a little vise-grip that comes in handy in club football; he yowled like a stuck pig and indignantly pronounced me 'a most bellicose individual'. "Where I come from, we call that the ass's bite", says I. He'll need no cilices for a while. He's not the only one. Surely such types are a liability and easily spotted, if you know what to look for. What's that you say? I should tell JJ? Not on your life.

18.8.52 : These monks are mighty preachers. The old men talk of the days before microphones, filling a big church and hopping every last syllable off the back wall. We have tough elocution classes, toning down the extreme accents, speaking with a bone-prop between the front teeth. We take turns practising our preaching in front of the whole community in English and Irish; some ordeal; the old hands take us apart. I feel like a wet rag after my turn; public speaking can hold no terrors after this. Demosthenes used to shout against the roar of the waves, with pebbles in his mouth. The old men well remember Percy French coming to give them lessons.

4.9.52 : Cavan are in the Final again. I can brag that I played with and against six of that team many a time. We were just across the border in Fermanagh but we always followed Cavan. The Blues were our team. What a thrill hearing them win the Ulster Final in Clones, and in my mind's eye, to be back again on the Hill with Dad, as in all the years we went on bicycles to see the Blues in action. God be with the days. Will they be able for Meath?

30.9.52 : Miracle of miracles; until the very last minute we didn't know whether JJ would let us listen to the All-Ireland or not. Somewhere inside that icy shell lurks a heart of flesh. I'm as cracked about football as ever; almost as hard saying good-bye to that as to my Bessy. I thought we were dead and buried when Carolan send over that wonder point from the corner flag, and we live to fight another day.

15.10.52 : So Cavan are the champions once again. A poor match, they say, dominated by the backs. The old wizard Higgins was the only forward they couldn't master. This will go down as Mick Higgins' All-Ireland, his swansong .... I get on well with everyone here although I'm close to no one. It wouldn't do. I'm a friendly loner, I suppose. However, I change into a sort of a lunatic the minute a match starts. It's my own team that get's me; can't stand anyone who doesn't try. JJ has warned me several times and I make resolutions, which I break again in the heat of battle .... They're coming out with new missals with the Latin on one side and English on the other. In the States they now say Holy Spirit instead of Holy Ghost. Our abominable punster couldn't resist, "Maynoothmen wont give up the ghost".

1.11.52 : BA exams looming; the pressure is on. It'll be great to have a degree in Greek and Latin on the missions. Seriously though, it's a chance in a lifetime to get into Catullus, Horace, Terence, Plautus and the Greeks especially, the stuff not on the curriculum. Here we are, holy monks, reading some of the rauciest stuff ever written, but no problem since it's classical. Another good thing, it has got me into the New Testament; some of it is very interesting in the original. First Corinthians, ch9, v5, reads as follows in the vulgate, 'Have we not power to carry about a woman, a sister, as well as the rest of the apostles?'. In the King James version it reads, 'Do we have no right to take along a believing wife, as do also the other apostles?'. The original Greek says,'adelphen gunaika, a sister woman'. What exactly did that mean to the writer at that time and in the place where he was writing?. In many cultures the woman means the wife. A note in the vulgate says, somewhat sententiously, that it refers to the band of women who followed Jesus and the apostles and attended to their needs; that this tradition continued. But that was a group; this refers to an individual woman associated in some way with each apostle personally. She may indeed have been a sort of maid; they may have been married; who knows at this remove? What is interesting is that this text is an obvious embarrassment for the Catholic translator; he is not above stretching things a bit, to safeguard the case for a celibate priesthood.. On the other hand, the Protestant bible would naturally be seeking biblical backing for a married clergy. With neither does truth seem to be a priority. It is also interesting that Paul goes on to mention Kephas, Peter, specifically, in the context, and we know that he was married; Jesus cured his mother-in-law. Another thing; Paul is making the

71

point that he himself is a great fellow, not above boasting a bit, because he has no 'adelphe gune' himself. He shouldn't be blowing his horn, for his writings show that that was no great hardship for him; Paul had no fondness for women. How truly human they turn out to be, when we cut through the accretions and preconceptions, and get down to the bedrock of what actually happened..

29.6.53 : Ten of us cycled down to Clifden; Paddy Mulvihill, a Mayoman, was the capo. Off we went in twos and Paddy gave orders that, whichever way we went, we were all to meet at Maam Cross for prayers and lunch. When Mutt and Jeff got near the rendezvous, they could here the laughing. Paddy and his partner got there first, it seems; it was already one o'clock and no one else was yet in sight and he got worried. An old English couple came along in their motor-car. Paddy flagged them down; he was worried enough to breach the code of silence, "If you see people dressed like us, please tell them we are here at Maam Cross. If you don't see them, you needn't bother". Paddy couldn't understand what all the laughing was about ....the old English lady said to her husband "How delightful, George, how typically Irish".   Got into football trouble again last week; lost my temper and it was duly reported to JJ, who hauled me in on the carpet, "Bro Polycarp, I would expect you to be giving better example. Your true colours come out on the football field; behind that charming smile I detect pride and arrogance. A monk must be humble instead of taking on himself to know more than his betters. Another display like that and you'll be off football for a month"; "Yes, Rev Fr. - I'm sorry, Rev Fr. It wont happen again, Rev Fr."

11.7.53 : As you know, some of the old monks join us in Clifden every year, for a bit of a holiday and to be available as confessors; we have to go to confession once a week. They are great company; kindly old men who wouldn't hurt a fly; mighty stories they have to tell. They were the terror of the country in their heyday. They tell us it gives them a new lease on life to be among the young fellas. How they glory in the oft-told chestnuts, that seem to grow with every telling; how they

72

sniffed out the poteen and poured it in the river and the fish got drunk; how they hounded the company-keepers and put the fear of God in them with a black-thorn stick; how they rattled the hardened sinners in their boots. And the jokes, "His lordship the bishop was getting home from a conference one night, him and his housekeeper, when, what d'ya know, the engine started boiling over. Lucky for him, there was a house nearby and he went over for a sup of water to cool the engine. When the woman of the house saw who she had, she was so overwhelmed by the sight of the bishop of the diocese on her doorstep that she gave him a whole bucketful of water. He proceeded to top up the car and flung the rest of the water in over the ditch. Out comes this ferocious litany of curses. "Watch your tongue", says the bishop, "I'll have you know, my good man, I have a lady here". "And what d'ya think I have here, a waterhen, ha ha ha". This year we have old crusty Fr. Con with us. He has it in for the Protestants. He claims there is a blackguard of a priest buried somewhere near here, who turned his coat and joined the soupers back in famine times. Has our heads light to take him to see the grave. We enquired from Willy and sure enough, the tombstone is in Ballyconneely graveyard. Fr. Con is very feeble; we brought him out in Willy's ass-and-cart. He stood looking at the grave, all covered with dandelions and thistles, as if he was praying. Then he started fumbling, "Shtand well back there, boys", says he, and he proceeded to spray the weed-bed. You never saw anyone so contented for the rest of the holidays. Human nature is a funny thing.

10.1.54 : Preaching, like politics, makes strange bedfellows. They let us hear the Rev Paisley on the wireless last week, as an example of the real thing. "I have to hand it to him", said one past master, "He has the nga and can put a skin even on a threadbare gospel like that; a real fire-and-brimstone man, he would have made a great missioner". A west-briton from Portadown has taken over the elocution class, and is hell-bent on digging out the bog accents, root and branch ... Fr Johnny home from the Philippines; gave us a talk about the missions. He had us in stitches one minute, spell-bound the next; the most

73

hair-raising bits about earthquakes and typhoons and head-hunters and women walking around, naked to the waist. In between the yarns, he played native tunes and snatches of Chopin and Beethoven on the mouth-organ. JJ's face, during the spicy bits, would make a cat laugh. We knew Johnny was laying it on a bit thick but no matter.

2.2.54 : Pope Pius X11 is going to define the assumption of Mary. It's a pity; a stumbling-block for ecumenism. We believe that Mary was assumed, body and soul, into heaven; that should be enough without a formal definition. I was lucky yesterday; blew up in the hurling match; I play in goals. It was a terrible day so maybe the pidgeon didn't venture out. Anyway, the ball came in high and I grabbed it, but the full back backed into me with his big fat arse and put me and ball and all in the net. "Holy fuck", says I, or words to that effect. I don't know where it came from; I was never fond of bad language. I'll have to watch it; might not be so lucky the next time.... Fr Pat explains how Trent was reactionary, reacted to Luther; tried to set everything in stone for all time. Instead, church, theology, everything, are based on Christ's cross, "Greater love than this no man hath than to lay down his life for his friend". The church is made up of people of flesh and blood. It is alive. The faith is not merely a body of formulae in the textbook, or in the head; it is in the hearts of living people; it is lived. The church is in a monolithic straitjacket.

Fr Pat knows Fr. Haring, who has re-written moral theology on the basis of love rather than law. He suffered under the Nazis and is now suffering under the Vatican, for his convictions. No one doubts Pius X11's good intentions; what is in doubt is his wisdom; his weakness is that he consults no one, wants to run the whole show himself; he could have come out stronger against Hitler had he rallied the moral support of the whole church behind him, instead of going it alone. Why cant he talk to Fr Haring, man to man? ... The latest news on the liturgy front is the dialogue Mass. Pius holds a tight grip on the tap, letting down a drip at a time; like the oul polly cow, who wouldn't let down her milk for anybody only Cissy singing the Coolin to her

.... Talking about well-meaning busybodies, in high or low places, I hold that old saw, 'The road to hell is paved with good intentions', to be an article of our faith. What's more, I can prove it. The Pelagians were condemned for heresy long ago, because they maintained that man could be saved by his own efforts alone. I would be burned at the stake if I said this out loud, but the plain unvarnished truth is that the modern popes, from Pius 1X to Pius X11, may mean well, but they have gone far beyond the mandate of their office. They have left the Holy Ghost out of the picture; they are Pelagians, trying to save the church by their own efforts.

16.4.54 : Got a month's suspension for bad temper and bad language on the football field. Got a lecture as well on pride and self-will and arrogance.. The monk cannot be indulging his passions, giving vent to his feelings; he cannot be wilful; he must yield up his liberty; he must be humble and live under obedience; he cannot have a mind or a will of his own "I am warning you that you will not be accepted as a suitable candidate for ordination to the priesthood, unless there is a marked improvement in this insolent, independent attitude of yours. You manage to keep it well hidden at other times under that smug smile; I've been watching you; you show your true colours on the football field".

13.7.54 : Clifden : Yesterday we were out in the big boat again. It was blowing quite fresh from the west and, with the sea going out, the waves were short and choppy, the colour of jade with white froth on top. Here and there a touch of brown, sometimes sea-weed, sometimes a seal poking his head up for a look. Less than a dozen of us like the sea; most are afraid of water, and pulling on a sweep is too much like hard work. Eight of us making for a desert island with a pot of spuds. The mackerel were hitting. I was back on Lough Erne trolling for pike. Six mile of steady work, lit a fire, boiled the Aran banners in sea water and grilled the macherel, a feast fit for a king. We split up and went exploring the island. Three of us found a little cove, stripped, and swam raw. Oh, the feel of the water on the skin, but a crazy chance to take. Were we spotted? Later we decided

75

to take another chance involving serious risk; took the boat out the narrow passage between this island-with-no-name and Inishboffin. After a tough haul in a racing sea we inched our way out into the open Atlantic, only three boat lengths between the rocks. "Next parish Boston", someone said. Now I know what 'rocked in the cradle of the deep' means.

23.12.54 : How very slowly the time passes. It is Christmas again, more than five years since I saw Mam or Dad or any of the family; six and a half since I left home. Three gone to Canada. Hard times in Ireland. The Dublin Opinion goes to town on Dev looking in at his green dream in his heart, while the most of the country goes threadbare and half-starved across the sea. I am ashamed in this cushy life; my vow of poverty is a cruel mockery of the real poor. Christ loves the poor; where do I stand? .... I get a chance to steal a decko at a paper on the QT once in a while; Myles na gCoppaleen is not afraid to call a spade a spade; cuts them all down to size ... Two and a half years to go to the big day.

22.2.55 : Our informer reminded me of a story still told around the islands of Lough Erne. There used to be a market every Saturday during the war at a spot on the border called Stackey's Haggard and the old mud-wall cabin was still there. People flocked there for white loaves and a pound of tea when the rationing in the Free State allowed only a half-ounce of tea a week and the bread was as black as your boot.. Here is one story I heard there. Shakum Malarey was a priest-hunter in the pay of the horse-sojers in the big barracks up the river at Belturbet. One day a girl looked out Stackey's window and says, "A Iosa, seo chagainn Shakum Malary". They ambushed him and stuck him like a pig and spiked him down in the lough. But the flood brought him up. Every place he floated in, the people pushed him out again. He is buried at the point of Gola. The big stone on top of him is there to this day.

21.3.55 : I had been a good boy on the football field for a long time. Even JJ admitted grudgingly that my conduct was exemplary. God knows I have been provoked. Patrick's Day is our big match, our All-Ireland. Ulster challenged the other three provinces and our main man let us down; stood gazing dreamily out over Galway Bay the entire first half. Me, I follow the Bible-man, a time for war and a time for peace, so I gave him a swift kick in the arse to waken him up. He never noticed, still away in cloud-cuckoo-land. I crashed into him by accident on purpose; still nothing. I started the litany and when I got to 'hoor's ghost', it must have hit a raw nerve. As luck would have it, the ball arrived just as he woke up. He knocked men down to left and right and buried the goalkeeper and the ball in the net. We won by a point. JJ was on the sideline; how could he have missed my high jinks. I'm afraid I'm sunk this time. Hasn't called me in yet; letting me stew for a while, no doubt. Am I really for the drop? How could I face home? It would kill Ma.

3.4.55 : It has been hell, waiting for JJ's watery eye to light on me any minute. Maybe all the cheering drowned my outburst, but I do seem to have escaped again, by a whisker .... Fr Pat says the day will surely come when the priest will say the Mass in English, facing the people. It's hard to believe. Every syllable of Latin, every rubric, every movement and gesture, are regarded as sacrosanct, the rubrics. It is very interesting to hear how power took over in the church, in the time of Constantine, about the year 313 AD, inspite of Christ's repeated warnings that they were not to 'lord it over others like the great ones of this world'. The church did not take over the pagan Roman empire, as the history books claim; the pagan civil authority in Rome took over the church. The clerical state had it's origins in the civil service of the pagan Roman empire. Thus politics reared it's ugly head in the church. It wouldn't do at all to put that kind of stuff in one's answer in a church-history exam, though it is the gospel truth.

5.5.55 : One of the old monks is known among us as Mr. McGregor. He goes by the book. The monastery wit asked what was the difference between McGregor and Joan of Arc ... "We give up". Answer: "Joan of Arc is Maid of Orleans; McGregor is made of wood". We had a discussion recently about the morality of modern dancing. The consensus was that, because of the body-contact, waltzing, fox-trotting, quick-stepping and such-like, are all immoral, because they are proximate occasions of sin. Mr. McGregor's opinion was that the danger could be reduced if the couples could be kept apart; they could then dance away to their hearts' content; it wouldn't even be a venial sin. The question was next raised, how far apart would they have to be. McGregor said, "About the width of a railway track". A man from Lisseycasey next asked, tongue in cheek, if the West Clare line would be wide enough .... A few of us go out once in a while to visit Irish-speaking families in Menloe. I'm getting used to the rhythm of Irish. It's great to get a little courage to say something and to be understood. Am getting to like Irish and to feel proud of our language. The fior-gaels turn everybody off, insisting that we must twist our thoats in knots, and keep hawking and spitting or it's not the real McCoy.

29.6.55 : Our canon law man also goes strictly by the letter. He boasts that he has never read a book on any subject but canon law, in his entire life. He's even more wooden than old McGregor. He presented the following case to us, as an example of how exciting canon law can be. A certain couple were getting married, as usual in the bride's parish, and invited a priest-friend by the name of Fr. John Smith to perform the ceremony. Faculties were got, all was in order. It happened that the PP had to go on a sick-call and returned to find the wedding party leaving the church, but, to his horror, it was a different Fr. John Smith. So, of course, the couple weren't properly married at all. He rushed after them, caught up with the car, got them out on the side of the road and married them again. About a year later he was travelling that road with a friend and was relating the story. He stopped the car. "This is the very spot where I married them", he said. "But this is not in your parish", said the other man. They still weren't married. Can you believe it? Talk about debating about how many angels could fit on the head of a pin

19.9.55 : Although we are a browbeaten, downtrodden lot, we have our secret little revenges once in a while. It is an old classical tradition to best the professor. What a joy it is when the class turns the tables on the teacher. You must set and bait the trap carefully. The west-briton who teaches us elocution and English is a superior type, but weak on Latin and knows no Greek, so he's wide open to ambush. Somebody asked innocently in class, "Where does the word 'sex' come from?". He fell for it. He explained, in that superior tone of his, that, of course, sex means six in Latin; obviously it comes from the sixth commandment, "Thou shalt not commit adultery". Mutt spoke up, "Rev Fr, that means Cicero read the Old Testament, for he uses the term 'sexualis'. Maybe he had Jewish friends who taught him the Ten Commandments. "How very interesting", said the reverend professor, not realising his leg was being pulled. With little triumphs like this we strive to perk up our days at the grindstone. With our innocent pranks we pin-prick the pompous; for it is a long haul and we are usually at the receiving end.

30.11.55 : I was in with JJ yesterday for the monthly private confab. I'm definitely not one of his favourites but he was civil enough. It seems he got instructions from on high to quiz us about any sexual problems we might have. I really felt sorry for the poor man; it was killing him, "Do impure thoughts bother you?; What about dreams? Are your feelings sometimes aroused?'. How would he have taken it if I had said my unruly member had a mind of his own? He was plainly relieved to get back onto a safe spiritual footing, but he did prescribe a remedy for more physical matters, "A cold shower and a vigouous rub-down with a rough towel., and you'll be as right as rain".

24.12.55 : Christmas once more. It's a long haul and I'm fagged out, not physically but mentally. The strain of all the studies and the stress of making a lifelong commitment soon. In a few months I'll be a deacon and that'll be it. Am I doing the right thing? A bunch of men all cooped up together under spartan rules, it's like a hen-house, brings out the worst. The vast majority are decent people with loose tongues; just enough really bad eggs to spoil the whole basket.; the complete gamut, deep spirituality, backbiting, envy, plain vindictiveness, austerity, luxury, kindness, selfishness, prayer, all living cheek by jowl. And we have a few tulips, right under JJ's nose and he never smelled them. Reminds me of the B-specials back home pulling you for no light on your bike, but they cant catch the big fish. I came charging into the printing room the other morning to find a balding fellow up to no good with a youth. He seemed to be trying to strangle him, and he obviously did not welcome my rude intrusion one little bit.. One of the old retired men, who spent most of his life in the Philippines, was telling us as a funny joke, about a man who applied to enter the order out there. When pressed as to his motive, he said, "I likes men". At least he was honest.

4.4.56 : The IRA are back on the war-path; attacked Armagh barracks. A few here are die-hard republicans. Sean South from Limerick was an altar-boy. The north-south thing and partition more complicated than ever. We have some fierce debates and rows about it here. Dad always said that it would have been settled in spite of England, only for the church's stand on mixed marriages. In my book, both sides are victims, in their own way. Protestants and Catholics are discouraged by church and state, each from getting to know the other. I blame Dev and the Catholic bishops in particular; they should know better. Very few open minds in Ireland; how can the truth get in to make us free?

5.1.56 : Bill Haley from the Usa has hit London with a new type of music. They call it Rock-and-Roll.The old guard are horrified; diabolical; will sap the moral fibre. Heard Rock Around The Clock on the wireless; seems harmless enough to me.

5.17.56 : There is something in me that makes me the devil's advocate. I am pretty cold-blooded, a bit of a sceptic. God gave me a deep faith; I wouldn't be one for long prayers; Jesus says in one place 'no need for many words'. It's a question of being a man of your word. It's the Presbyterian drop in me. I would like to be remembered as an honest man; I don't worry about God's judgment; He will give me a fair crack of the whip. I do see better times ahead, but in the meantime, my major problem would be that, deep down, their Christian instinct makes people see many facits of the church as a scandal, a stumbling-block to faith. God has been very good to us; we have the great good fortune to know the church, in spite of all her wrinkles, as the beautiful face of Christ . What of those who, for whatever reason, see only the wrinkles and conclude; "This has to be the handiwork of a false god; how could the true God, if there is one, condone such things as human slavery and the inquisition in the past, or some of the present carry-on"?. Christ said He would not break the bruised reed; we are all bruised reeds. We should be able to see all the good the church does, but our vision can be obscured so that we can't see the wood for the trees. The new thelogy is aimed at reform; that we may not incur the curse of Christ, "If a man scandalises one of these little ones who believe in Me, it were better for that man that a millstone be tied around his neck and he be drowned in the depths of the sea". We must practise what we preach.

1.8.56 : Last Sunday was the big day for Croke Patrick. Four of us left Clifden at 4am and cycled the 50 odd miles to the foot of the reek; climbed in our bare feet in a wet mist; confession and Mass at the top. The journey back against a steady headwind was the toughest part. Won't be over it for a fortnight.

15.8.56 : It's now seven years since that day in 49 when Mrs Finn and Puck met us in the bedford; a lifetime. One more year to go. It's a long weary haul. I love the church; I'm a deacon now and the die is cast. But there are far too many things in the church that are a disgrace. I mean disgrace literally because these scandals, road-blocks, prevent the grace of God getting to people. Christ died on the cross for all humankind; He left the church in the world to make Him known to every generation. His purpose and mission are frustrated, crippled, by our carry-on. How can church leaders not see that politics has no place here? Look at the attitude of most Catholics, most priests, to Protestants. What about freedom of conscience? We read in the textbook that freedom is essential in the human act, as for example in marital consent. But people are not free in practice. Christ was gentle; He treated people with respect; He invited, He

81

never coerced. Our doctrine is fine but we do not follow it in practice; "These people honour me with their lips but their hearts are far from me". Control is the name of the game. Is there not some truth in what ordinary people say, and they not all anti-clerical, that the church sides with the rich and power-ful? Some of the clergy are kind; many of them look down on the lay-people. It is terrible to think that many, especially women, grow up afraid of the priests. No one was afraid of Christ; He was kind to all, in particular to the children. Why must we square off into liberal and conservative camps? Should we not all be seeking the truth, praying for the grace to be open to the Holy Ghost? Only God can open the eyes of the soul. Fr Pat agrees; him I have to thank. I always loved the truth; thanks to him I now know that it is not wrong to search for the truth, no matter where it leads. Is it not strange that in this year of Our Lord, 1956, in an Irish seminary, one cannot discuss these mat-ters openly, for fear of being labelled a radical? Even Fr Pat, now silenced by all the bishops of Ireland at Michael of Galway's behest, has to be careful what he says in class. The witch-hunters are out beating the cover for modernists and we, so near ordination, must tread very gingerly. Mum's the word.

3.1.56 : We are learning how to say Mass, practising the rubrics. Saying the office is a delight; it's a pity other selections of scripture are not included; our choice is limited. The office takes me an hour and a half most days, a heavy chore to be fit-ted in with all the studies and other exercises; some seem to be speed-merchants; we're supposed to form the words with the lips and not merely read mentally. I'm told a big percentage of priests don't know enough Latin to understand what they are reading; surprising until one thinks about it. Scholarship was not a priory except for the few, until after the war. Fr Pat is hopeful that the Mass and breviary will be in the vernacular in our lifetime. We know that Rome moves slowly when she does move; no sign yet. A strange thing; vocations are down this year for the first time and not only with us.

10.4.56 : A bit of an argument going on lately between theology and canon law on the subject of marriage. Six of the sacraments are in the dogmatic theology textbook; not a word there on marriage, which is covered entirely in canon law. The one says the essence of marriage is a contract, a legal matter; the other says it is the bond of love between the man and woman; no love, no marriage. Canon law says once the contract is entered freely and is sealed by the consummation of the marriage act, it cannot be broken. Theology says love can be born and die; there is a valid marriage only where both parties are mature enough to make a lifelong commitment. Where this is absent, or ceases to exist, there is no marriage. Looking at it this way opens the door to divorce. Theology goes back to St. Paul who says that the sacrament of Christian marriage is modelled on Christ's love for His church, 'until death do us part'. Can a marriage die? Is divorce forbidden by Christ's teaching in all circumstances? A big question.

14.5.56 : I am reading Schillebeeckx; it seems so obvious that the church is made up of people; of course it is, and that includes the priests, bishops and the pope. That's all very well in theory; in practice the clerics are a class apart from the laity. He says it is a mindset which we have inherited; we think of the church as the institutions rather than the people; we think exclusively instead of inclusively. Not easy to find solitude here; I miss the bog.

20.7.56 : In Clifden once more. The weather is wild; nothing to do but read. The Quakers in Pennsylvania decided to release their slaves. It came about because one of their number spoke out publicly against slavery in their weekly prayer meeting; the Quakers are allowed to pray out loud. God had wakened his conscience; he in turn wakened their consciences. This man died young; five years after his death the slaves were freed. The Jesuit order in Pennsylvania likewise had slaves and individual members also spoke out against slavery, but it took more than 70 years more, before action was taken. Finally the Jesuits sold their slaves; they did not free them, nor did they concern themselves with their subsequent fate. In which of these two did the light of Christ shine?

1.9.56 : During the reign of the Emporor Constantine, Christianity became the state religion of the Roman Empire. Shortly before, it did not pay to be a Christian; you could get fed to the lions. Now suddenly, it did not pay to be a pagan, you could just as easily get fed to the lions. Mass conversions were the order of the day. Reading between the lines of church history, one is tempted to ask, "How many joined the church out of conviction, how many out of convenience? Was it a matter of saving one's soul or one's skin or one's job?". Be that as it may, the fact is that power and politics entered the church at that time. Before that Christians had been nobodies. Now the important people took over and remodelled the church along the lines of the imperial civil service. The price the church paid for getting tied into the state, for getting status, was the loss of her liberty. Never again, even to this day, would Christ's church be free.

20.12.56 : The time is getting near. We have been called for mission. Each one is called by name, individually. God puts the thought that draws, into one's heart. We must always be listening for He can call again any time He wants. If anyone comes, by some odd quirk of fate, to read this, he will say that I do a lot of complaining. It is true; some things in this life of ours are downright wrong, diametrically opposed to the mind and spirit of Christ. I put up with them to get to the priesthood. I pray that the day will come soon when they are rooted out. Other things can be improved. Many things are wonderful, beautiful; I thank God for my vocation. In spite of the repressive regime and the few bad apples, most of the monks are decent men, according to their lights. May the day dawn when it will no longer be a crime to have a mind of one's own .... Even to myself I sound like a real sore-head; always complaining. But in all honesty, it bothers me that people can be content with so much mediocrity in the church. So many things in our wonderful church could be so much better. It is a sad day when people find God in spite of us. Better days ahead, please God, if Fr. Pat is right.

16.1.57 : Fr. Provincial comes once a year to sees how things are going. Beforehand he wrote, suggesting that we discuss among ourselves any improvements we might come up with. I thought it would be a good idea if the lay-brothers be allowed to listen to a football game on Sundays. All agreed. When the time came the Provincial asked for our suggestions. For once cagey Jeff left himself wide open. I spoke up. He stared at me as if I had suddenly gone astray in the head; "Completely out of the question; anything else?" he dismissed me curtly.. Not one man had the gumption to support me; they left me hanging out to dry. I was furious, not least at myself, and told them what I thought of their bravery. I had learned a painful lesson, dont stick your neck out.

2.3.57 : The pidgeon has flown off to Rome to study canon law. He wont be missed. It's hard to believe that a seminary would encourage spying. I hear bishops do it too, will even read anonymous letters. Shame on them .... That's the problem with being an idealist - one expects the highest common factor from humans, when the best we can hope for is the lowest common denominator. The average person is away below average; dont ask too much and you wont be disappointed. But I just cant help wanting the very best for the church, because I love her. It kills me to see her beautiful face so disfigured.

5.6.57 : Jughead disappeared in the night; not a word. He had only a few months to go to ordination. The order does not have to give him or anyone else a reason for his dismissal. It is very hard after all these years and so near ordination. If he is determined to persevere in his vocation, he will be taken by a diocese in England or the States. I hope they give him a decent reference; I doubt that he committed any serious crime. On second thoughts, maybe he went of his own free will, but why would he wait this long? The big day is the fifteenth of September; time flying now.

21.7.57 : This is our last year in Clifden; I'll miss it. Every chance we get we're out on the water. four of us cycled to Killary Harbour, crossed in a currach and climbed Maolraoi. Less than a month now to ordination. Eleven of us. As well as the family and relations, I have invited some of the neighbours I have known since I was a child. Not only a priest in the family but a priest from the townland, makes them all proud. After 8 years we're getting three days at home. A neighbour who has an old prefect has offered to drive me around on land, and I'll have a fleet of cots to ferry me on the water. I intend to give the blessing in every house I ever stood in, Catholic, Protestant and Dissenter; I'll be busy. Vocations away down again this year; no one knows why.

12.8.57 : I'll be ordained a priest in 3 days' time, by Michael of Galway the bishop with his nose permanently out of joint; he seems to be continually smelling a bad smell, someone said of him. The priesthood and the Mass, that's the main thing. I'm trying hard to let nothing spoil it, but we got a nasty shock yesterday. We were told, out of the blue, that only members of the immediate family could be seated in the chapel for the ceremony. It seems every VIP in Ireland has been invited; that leaves no room for family and friends. Much cribbing. No change out of Old Woodenhead. When I heard it I was fit to be tied. Calmed down and said to myself, "To hell with them; I'm not going to let on; let them all come'. Some of the lads are going to keep an eye out for me and make sure whoever comes gets in.

20.8.57 : Just got back from home; dog-tired. It will take a long time for these last four days to sink in, hardly a wink of sleep; I visited every house I never stood in. Whole Protestant families knelt on the heartstone for my blessing. i was humbled by their faith. A presbyterian tractor pulled the old prefect back out of the gripe I landed her in. I'll never forget it.... Any day now the new assignments will be posted on the board, who's going where? I want to go to the Philippines but dont dare hope. It's in the lap of the gods. Can only pray that the Holy Ghost will plant the thought in their heads to send me there. For nearly eight years I have been asking Mary to put in a good word for me. It is a most wonderful thing to say Mass every day. No words can describe it. No need to take notes; I'll never get used to it.

1.9.57 : I went down on my knees; can't believe it; I'm going to the Philippines. Blue Funnel Line out of Liverpool in ten days' time. Going home tomorrow for a few more days and then we're off. Poor Mutt; inspite of his best efforts not to shine, he is doomed to Rome and a life of teaching. I'm going with Fr. Peter who is returning to PI. He warned me not to talk about it; I didn't know why. Now I know. The nuns in Cork got wind of it and have saddled us with a load of freight and baggage for their sisters in Leyte.

15.11.57 : Bessy came all the way up to Liverpool to see me; we had a few hours, walking in the park, talking of old times and the new Rock and Roll sensation here called the Beatles. A sad parting; we go our separate ways. She has an English boy-friend. I saw her to her train; no histrionics; we just shook hands. So that's that; shin shin, mar a deartha as gaeilge .... The voyage would take a book to tell, Biscay, Med, Suez, Indian Ocean, South China Sea; time stands still at sea. Bought a har-monica for five pound in Change Alley in Singapore; Fr. Peter taught me two tunes, Danny boy and Annie Laurie. The heat in the tropics is terrific; seeps through your clothes. Manila's smells are a rich concoction, all the variations blended, from the sublime to the sewer. The cicadas are deafening; they say one gets used to them. Our luggage was unloaded on the dock for the customs to check. "Who's?", asked the wee man, eyeing the mighty crate. Fr. Peter owned up. The man looked doubtful, took a pinch-bar out of the hand of a helper and prised up a slat. He reached down into the depths, groped around and a know-ing look flitted across his face. He held up his find and peered through it at the tropical noonday sun., "Your's, Padre?". It was a lovely big pair of pink bloomers, no doubt destined for the nether parts of the Reverend Mother. "Segue", says the wee man, without batting an eye, stuffed them back in and whacked on the slat, "Muy bien, no hay problema, Padre", with a rascal-ly twinkle in his eye.

Chapter 7

1.12.57 : Leyte, PI; things have been so hectic I never got a chance or the privacy to write till now. I like the people here, they are very friendly. The voyage would fill a book. A freighter with 12 passengers; the weather was beautiful, except a bit rough in the Bay of Biscay. Five weeks to Singapore; time stands still at sea. Bought a harmonica in Change Alley; old Fr. Peter is going out for the third time. He taught me how to play Danny Boy. Getting the hang of it; I'll never be able to play like him. Got a letter from Mutt in Brazil. How on earth did he get out there? That Kerryman hasn't a long head on him for nothing. Rome was killing him. To add salt to the wound he knew the pidgeon was watching his every move and reporting back. One more wicked thought entered that long head of his. He did a little sleuthing of his own when he got the pidgeon out, typed up a letter on his typewriter, painting himself in the blackest colours, signed the pidgeon's name to it and sent it off to Ireland. Nobody smelled a rat; soon orders came; Mutt was on a plane for South America. It was too late when they tumbled to it. Best of all, they didn't want to admit anything, so there wasn't one word about it, 'hoist with his own petard'. He says the first thing he has to do is teach the people how to plough the way they do in Kerry .... I am learning the language. Started by hearing the children's confessions. Fr. Sennett from Belfast took me out on my first mission. Learning fast. I have two little sermons off by heart in Waray-Waray and am getting the hang of the lingo by asking questions. We are staying with the priest, who has a houseful of nieces and nephews. When we first arrived, he put his head in through the curtain and called something in to the kitchen. "What is he saying?", I asked; "He is telling the cook to put more water in the soup". We were going around the barrio with the landrover and a loudspeaker, persuading the people to come to the mission and urging the couples living together to get married. An old woman stuck her head in the window of the landrover and mumbled something about the PP. "What is she saying?", I asked. "She says she'll get married if the PP agrees to get married as well". I'm learning fast; that explains all the nieces and nephews.

1.1.58 : Imagine swimming in a warm sea on New Year's Day. This in where the Americans landed when MacArthur kept his word and came back to drive out the Japs in '44. Rusting hulks of ships and military vehicles litter the water and the beach. A girl from our choir married a senator called Marcos last year. Her name was Imelda Romualdez before she married; first cousin of the Governor .... Every man here is armed to the teeth; life is cheap. When someone gets up a bit in the world, the first thing he must do is get a gun, for self-defence. The ordinary five-eighth has to make do with a bolo. Some strum the guitar; some sleek their gamecock; all have bolos, always within reach. It's for self-protection more than for aggression, for slights are not easily forgotten or forgiven. A man wouldn't dream of leaving his house without strapping on his weapon, just like John Wayne. He keeps it by his head at night; he wears it ploughing with his carabao. The Waray-Warays have the name here of being slow with the tongue but swift with the blade; kamatay-on means death; before he gets to the third syllable, you're history.

18.2.58 : In the mountains the houses sit on stilts; split bamboo floors and nipa-palm roofs; very cool and dry. The four corner posts, called haligis, are from a tree that no termite or rot will attack. Another tree is so hard that no saw or axe will cut it; it can only be felled by burning repeated rings of fire round it. When split, it is used for dowels. Sea-going ships and boats and canoes used to be built without a single metal nail being used. I am learning fast. Mahogany is a generic term covering a variety of tropical hardwoods. I saw a crucifix made from a tree that is now extinct. I enquired about a large wooden casket, beautifully carved, which formed the table of an altar in a house. This is common. They misunderstood, thinking I was asking what was in the box and replied, "grandpa". So I learned that a custom still lingers from pre-Christian times in remote areas, of embalming the body and keeping it in the home for some time after death. This is mistakenly labelled ancestor-worship. It is more correctly a mark of family solidarity.

17.3.58 : Three of us went to a place called Carigara in north Leyte. After a week in the town we split up to do the barrios, 3 days in each barrio; my first time on my own. I marched off into the mountains for 2 months with my bodyguard of lads carrying the Mass-kit, religious articles, change of clothes and the tape-recorder and various bits and pieces. Very beautiful scenery, coloured birds and exotic flowers, orchids hanging from the mountainsides. Chattering monkeys, these islands are volcanic, each has a rice-growing plain around the coast and steep mountains in the centre; no roads. Some mountain rice grown. All kinds of fruits grow wild, many varieties; bananas, papaya, star-apple, passion-fruit, durian, many more; I dont yet know the names of some. Durian is delicious, once you get past the smell of rotting flesh; but the mango is king. You stay with a family, sleeping with them on mats on the floor, sharing their food. The staple is rice and fish. The house is up on stilts. No electricity; no toilets. The day begins at 4:30am. Hundreds of huge torpedolike shells were lobbed into the mountains during the battle of Leyte Gulf; an empty shell-case is now the capilla bell and it's clanging carries far in the still air. Points of light begin to appear here and there. Now they start to move. They join to form little streams of light flowing down, merging into rivers. Then you hear a faint sound like angels singing. It is the aurora, men, women and children carrying torches, praying and singing the rosary, lights and shadows playing among the forest trees. The morning is full, confessions, Mass, baptisms, instructions, visiting the homes and the blessed siesta. In the evening is the sermon; then we all gather round for a meal and fun with the tape-recorder. Everyone must hear his or her own voice. The last night is the grand finale, the marriages. The Legion of Mary have been rounding up the strays, young ones, parents and grandparents who never managed to get hitched up. Number of couples depend on the size of the barrio. The fourth morning everything is packed up and a band of young men escort me to the next barrio. It could be a ten-mile trek by steep mountain paths through the forest, or a short walk between the rice-paddies, where white cranes wade, or ride on the backs of the carabao, searching for ticks, spearing flies and frogs. We arrived in a place high in the mountains called San Joachin. On the last night a boy and girl got married. This was different because they had not yet come together. We sang and danced to the music of guitars; plenty to eat and tuba to drink, a mild drink gathered every morning from the top of the cocoanut palm. What fun we had with the tape-recorder. In the night they woke me up to a terrible sight. The young girl-bride sat on the floor, the boy's head in her lap, his blood stark against her white dress. I anointed him and he died. In the pale light of morning we passed their new house of bamboo and nepa; blood stained the young rice sprouting before the door. It was a lonesome sight.

19.7.58 : Back at base for a short break. Just heard the news that the pope is dead. He was a good man according to his lights but an autocrat; he exceeded his mandate; he and St. Paul would have had words. I dont like this cult of 'the Holy Father'. Who's the next pope going to be, a non-Italian, an American? The betting here is on Montini. When one comes down to earth, it's naive to hope for much change in the church; it's run by Pius' men .... A teacher came to see me; I noticed her in church. It's a small world; when we got talking we discovered that her neighbour is married to my sister Maggy in Toronto. She came to ask me if I could help her to get her passport. She wants to go to Canada to study to become a doctor. It's wellnigh impossible for ordinary people here to get a passport. I'll ask Geromino; maybe he'd put in a word with Imelda for her, whatever good that might do. Geronimo used to live next door to Imelda's family here; they were as poor as church mice. She is very beautiful, the girl I mean.

4.8.58 : Who on earth is this Cardinal Roncali; no one ever heard of him. He's very old; at his age nothing is going to happen in the church for another while; we can only slog away and pray for miracles. Now I see how ridiculous it is to be saying Mass in Latin for these poor people, who have enough magic of their own. The Philippines has been Catholic for nearly 400 years and they have not yet got one saint of their own or even a blessed; obviously they're not a priority in Rome. Now if it was an Italian ... I'm learning; for the first 150 yrs a Filipino could not become a priest; for the next 150 yrs a Filipino priest could not run a parish; they only got a native bishop in the last hundred years; they still have no cardinal. I was thinking; maybe there's more to the new pope than meets the eye. Could the name, John XX111, be a kind of a sly joke, poking fun at himself? Maybe he has a sense of humour, is halfway human .... Got word that Bessy is married; said Mass for her and her husband; he became a Catholic. Goodbye, Bessy, you and I have travelled far apart but we'll always be friends.

10.9.58 : Flew for the first time; dont like planes, though they tell me the DC-3 is the safest plane flying. The havoc greedy man wreaks. Coming in over the coast of Mindanao when it's raining would bring tears from a stone. The overwhelming thought is heart's blood oozing. Brown and red and yellow streaks fan far out to sea. The rain is leaching the country's heart's blood out into the Pacific. The very land is pouring into the sea. Some political crony, a staunch Catholic of course and a pillar of the community, has got a licence to log the virgin forest out of a face, to sell for plywood to Japan and to make him a millionaire. No roots left to hold the topsoil; no young trees planted. Some islands are already stripped naked to the bare rock. No trees, the clouds sail over and no rain falls and the wind blows away what is left in dust. Mindanao is a bit bigger than Ireland. The coastal Christians and the loggers push in on the Moslems; the ring of fire ever tightens round the poor misfortunate aborigines in the centre. Hell breaks loose and Manila sends in the army. Magsaysay squelched the communist Huks in Luzon in the 50's; no wonder they're coming back stronger than ever, and the 2 million Moslems in Mindanao want independence. The first chance I get I'm going in there to see for myself. Population of PI : 35 million; adding a million a year. This is some country; more than 7 thousand islands; will grow anything all year round. Seas full of fish. Drawbacks; humid heat, snakes and mosquitos. Rich too in minerals. Dirt roads along the coast. Friendly people; hospitable; slow to forgive, but they admit it because at least they're honest; we never forgive; we only think we do. Cities spawning shanty-towns with little industry or work. Land owned by rich families; the rest(90%), are tenants living hand to mouth. National craze, cockfighting. In the mercado you can buy anything under the sun for a pittance. A leaf of tobacco for a halfpenny will do you for a week. Roll you own tustus. Some of the old women are serious smokers, with the lit end inside the mouth. Men and women chew betel-nut with tan-bark, which stains the gums, would turn your stomach; not pretty when they grin and spit. House lizards live on the ceilings; part of the furniture. No heavy drinking, a little makes them tipsy; they have a mild drink called tuba. Steps are cut in the cocoanut palm; every morning the tuba-gatherer climbs with his long bamboo tube on his back. By evening the liquid has fermented slightly. San Miguel beer, brewed in Manila, is excellent..

6.10.58 : Immergency call to the hospital; took the motorbike. What a mess, like a slaughter-house; a fight with bolos, which are machetes forged from a car spring. Wading in blood. A nurse was measuring the length and depth of wounds with a carpenter's tapemeasure, calling out the numbers as she went, and a little man licked a stubby pencil and jotted them down in a grubby notebook, for the record I suppose. Before I left, one of the warriors was up on his feet walking around, showing off his rows of stitches all over his chest and shoulders like crazy strands of rag-wire. A night to remember; heading home for bed and a black pig shot out and took my front wheel with him. Soft landing in the acachia bushes ... You learn something new every day. The last mission I was on, the local lads pulled a fast one on me ; they all had a good laugh. They have a kind of men's club in the barrio, where they meet to drink a lttle tuba, train gamecocks, play the guitar; women need not apply. For special occasions they will capture a dog, give him nothing but water for a week. Then they make up a mixture of rice, herbs and spices and feed him till he's fit to burst. Then they hit him over the head and roast him on a spit, as is. Not letting on, they invited me to sample this concoction. Then they told me. It tast-ed pretty good, I must say. The real delicacy here is balut; boiled, half-hatched duck-eggs; that I haven't indulged in yet, to my knowledge. In Moslem countries at sunset, the muezzin can be heard, calling the faithful to prayer. Wherever they hap-pen to be they prostrate right there towards Mecca and pray to Allah. Every evening here, one also hears the mournful call in the growing darkness, "Balut, balut", as the vendor wends his way from street to street with his half-hatched duck-eggs.

15.12.58 : Roly-poly Pope John has surprised everyone. The word is that the Vatican boys dont like his style, too free and easy, he ignores their precious protocol and waddles off on his merry way to have a chat with ordinary people. Miracles never cease; the world has fallen in love with the pope, because he is human .... Geronimo is the old lay-brother; what stories he has. He and his mother lived next door to Imelda's family before the war. Imelda's father was shiftless; the poor branch of the most powerful family in Leyte they were. Imelda always had fierce drive to get on. Even as a little girl she was up first, her wood-en baclas echoing on the boardwalk as she hurried off to the mercado to buy a little rice and dried fish for the family.... Some Filipinos, only some, are light-fingered; anything that's not tied down is there for the taking. The Spaniards taught them 9 com-mandments in 400 years, all but the 7th; it didn't take the Japs long; cut off a hand the first time. They would always cut off a Moslem's right hand; the reason, in Islamic culture the right hand is for dignified activities such as eating; the left is for less dignified uses; for the rest of his life the Moslem thief has to eat like a dog. Geronimo was telling me how he joined up in the order. No foreign order took Filipinos until after the war. When he was refused in 1934, he stayed on anyway, helping in the kitchen for nothing. The Japs put all the Irish in concentration camps because they all had British passports. Geronimo would visit them in prison, bringing them food and books. Old Fr George, who was in the PI for over forty years and never went back to Ireland even for a holiday, took it on himself to receive Geronimo into the order in the concentration camp.

18.1.59 : Battista ran away and Castro has taken over Cuba. We keep abreast of world affairs with the short-wave radio and Time magazine. The big sugar barons here are delighted because, with Cuba closed, the price of sugar has shot up. It's an ill wind .... The Yanks are beginning to smell commies under Castro's bed; they and the Vatican have communism on the brain. ..... I see that teacher once in a while at Mass; she is from Samar; back again after the holidays. We were cooped up all those years; now the sudden freedom is frightening. No one looking over one's shoulder any more, to see or know what you do; prayers. modesty of the eyes, wild thoughts, all up to one-self now. Her beauty scares me. When she sees me she looks up, hoping I might have some news for her about the passport. We have talked a couple of times. If I am ever up that way, I am to make sure to visit her mother. Not a word yet about the pass-port; she cares about nothing else only becoming a doctor and coming back to her own people.

26.1.59 : My head is in a spin; we just heard on the wireless that Pope John has called a Council. All sorts of wild ideas flash through my mind. Will the new theology get a hearing? Will there be sweeping changes? How sweeping? Do I believe in omens? The door-bell rang; there she was, her eyes dancing; at long last there was movement on her passport. Warned her not to get her hopes too high; many a slip; I'm happy for her. My brain is in a whirl .... The blacksmith made me a bolo; I watched him forging it, a work of art. The Americans smuggled in facto-ry-made bolos to the underground resistance during the Japanese occupation but they weren't worth a damn for hack-ing through undergrowth or anything else; couldn't hold an edge. The real thing is forged from the spring-leaf of a car or truck; an all-purpose tool; it can shave you, slice a papaya, cut bread or sugar-cane, hack through a fair-sized tree, split fire-wood, sharpen a pencil, open a man to the navel.

23.2 59 : Just got back from Zamboanga where the rubber trees grow. Had a most astounding experience one night there; cant bring myself to put it down on paper; maybe later .... The pro-duction of rubber is fascinating; a cut is made in the side of the tree and the stuff flows out like milk. It is collected every day .... Though life is cheap (They say only 10% of the killings ever get in the papers), the priest is in little danger here, as long as he is recognised. It is safer in some areas to wear the full outfit, or at least to have it handy if slogging through the mountains. No bandit, cut-throat or pirate, Christian or Moslem or pagan, will touch the holy man, not out of respect so much as to avoid the bad luck it might bring. So we get the benefit of the doubt; we survive on superstition; you can be mighty glad of it in a tight spot .... Our next mission is in a place called Barongan in Samar; they say the parish is as big as an Irish county .... Haven't seen that teacher since I got back from the land of the rubber trees, although I have found myself thinking of her when I least expect it. Suppose ... but it's madness to suppose.

28.4.59 : We have started the mission in Barongan. That girl got her passport and will be leaving for Canada at the end of July. She's walking on air. As it happens, she comes from a bar-rio in this parish by the name of Ando. Will Ando be on my list? I'm between two minds about wanting to go or not; the thought is exciting and it's frightening, to have time alone with her. The fact is, I like her. I told her to go to Maggy when she reaches Toronto, and wrote to Maggy about her. Things not good between Maggy and Raul; a pity they have no children.

15.5.59 : Very busy but still plenty of time to think, too much time. For example, travelling in the mountains the paths are often steep, single file, no chance to talk; fording a river doesn't make for conversation; or riding on a swimming bull water-buf-falo when the water is too deep or the currents too strong for

96

wading. Serious conversation is naturally limited here, even at the best of times, although everybody has already heard stories about the old pope walking about Rome, talking to the ordinary people.. Pope John is calling the council in 1962 for the reform of the church. What is meant by reform? What will be changed and how much? What is the church anyway? Will the reform be radical? ... 'radical' comes from the Latin 'radix', meaning 'root'; will the reform, or renewal, go to the root? Will they go back to the gospel, to the way Christ set up the church?. The Son of Man, the Kingdom of God; He came to serve; He died for all; is the church the Kingdom of God ? How much of the new theology will seep through? At the start the church had nothing; would it be a good or bad thing it the church lost every thing? Should the church be poor? Exciting times. Now that change is in the air it frightens me. I know I have been ducking it but it's coming home to me; what if priests are allowed to marry, say 10-15 years from now? It's talked of. Even old wooden Mr. McGregor, away back in '54, amazed us all when he said that he would have married if Rome had allowed it. And the wag said, "Who would take him?". Many priests here are married in practice. Monogamy, meaning being faithful to the one woman, is very strict. Among them even the upper classes here are proud to have priests in their family tree. Maybe that is saying something to the rest of us.

4.7.59 : It turned out that Ando is an island three miles out in the Pacific; no one wanted to go out on the open sea in a canoe, so I got it by default. That teacher hadn't got her holidays yet, but I stayed with her mother and the grandparents. What a place; I could easily imagine settling there for the rest of my days. The canoe was waiting at the beach; they gave me a paddle and off we went. Ando is about the size of Goladuff, a bit of the coral reef sticking up out of the water; 65 families. It is utterly unspoiled, as God made it; parrots and mackaws and birds of paradise flit among the palms and acachia trees; every shape and colour of orchid and exotic flower and plant, hang from the rocks. I came for three days and stayed ten. High tide sweeps the fish-fry inside the reef, where the sharks can't follow. At night the men, women and children wade in the sea, thick as soup, and scoop them up in baskets, to be pickled and eaten raw. Fires along the shore; guitars strumming; children laughing as they plash in the sparkling sea, and the flying-fish streak off into the wind on wings of fire. There are huge caves under the highest part of the island where thousands of fruit-bats hang in rows .... They bury their dead on a shelf of rock near the entrance of the caves, in big Chinese jars; I wonder how far back in time they go, maybe even before Spanish times. Beyond the jars, bones and bits of broken pottery are stacked neatly. The burial custom here is to embalm the body and keep it for a time in a special wooden container in the house. One night a canoe came out of the darkness into the firelight; the teacher was home. All she could talk about was Toronto, and I listened. She had been saving for years, hoping against hope; now she was all set; had it all figured out. She would never marry, never have children. I heard this with mixed feelings of dismay and relief. In spite of myself I had begun to find myself toying with the idea of her and me. That settled that; or did it? When she comes back a qualified doctor, say ten years from now, who knows? I will always remember her walking in the sea in a long white dress. The guitars were moaning and she sang along, "Gugma ko, ngano ba intawon naglimbong ka?". We went into the caves twice without disturbing the bats; the first human being to get inside my guard. And so we parted. I could not bring myself to write down her name until now; goodbye Esther, till we meet again .... Terrible the waves of guilt that sweep over me and she was only laughing.

3.8.59 : Esther sent me a postcard from Hawaii; she's in the seventh heaven. Who knows what the future may bring; I can only live in hope ... Spanish names are common here; it's part of the culture of conquest. For example, the name Aguirre is Spanish. But in Samar I came across Maguirre, pronounced Mageery; they are very big in the export of copra, that is processed cocoanut for soaps and cosmetics. The name stretched across the front of a huge warehouse in Barongan, visible for miles out to sea, It had a familiar look about it, and sure enough, Maguirre turned out to be none other than the Irish name, Maguire. How did this Fermanaghman manage to wind up so far from home? It's tempting to speculate. There is a tradition that Columbus stopped in Galway and took an Irishman on board, before setting out to find India by sailing west instead of east. Maybe this Maguire chap came with Majellan and, like him, got no further, except that Majellan ended up dead and Maguire was very much alive, and lasted long enough to leave his mark. .... Great excitement here among the Americans and Irish, about Senator Kennedy running for the Presidency. What a feather in their cap. The betting is that even Joe's money wont overcome the bigotry against the Catholics and the Irish. Look at Al Smith, say the skeptics.

31.10.59 : Geronimo has some great yarns about the old days. In Spanish times the monks in a monastery in Manila were annoyed with the abbot; he got on their nerves, never stopped pestering them about breaches of the rules. So they poisoned him. Another abbot missed his step in the dark and fell down the stairs and broke his neck. Did he fall or was he pushed? In more recent times there is Fr. Roca, who is well on in years but is still hale and hearty. He carries a gun, just to be on the safe side. One week morning he was saying Mass and a dog came into the church. Fr Roca doesn't like dogs. He turned round at the Orate Fratres and there was the dog with his leg cocked. His reverence reached in under his alb and pit-choo; he shot the dog stone dead. Then he turned back to the altar and continued "Oremus ...." Nobody passed any remarks ... No word from Esther; she is probably too busy to write.

5.1.60 : I can't understand why Esther never wrote; not even a card for Christmas. I suppose it's a case of 'out of sight, out of mind'. She has her own life to live now and I'm a silly fool, building castles in the air. Let begones be bygones; it's a good lesson; should have more sense .... Geronimo learned his English from a Dublinman and talks like Jimmy O'Dea doing

Biddy Mulligan. He was telling me another one about Fr Roca and his gun. The baptisms were lined up as usual one Saturday morning. He got into a squabble with one of the god-mothers; she wanted the bell rung for her god-child, but wouldn't come up with the two pesos extra. She waited her chance. She thought she had him when he started pouring the water. She sidled over and reached up for the rope of the bell. But he had his eye on her. Two slugs in the post over her head changed her mind for her, fast. He didn't even hiccup in the Latin. Geronimo can put a great skin on a story .... Once in a while the Irish and Americans get together for a meal and a game of cards. The new theology came up. The question was asked, "What would happen to the seal of confession, if priests could marry? How could he keep anything a secret from the wife?'.

4.7.60 : My first chance to write in many months. Terrible. Terrible. Esther is dead. A man appeared at the door one morning, a fortnight ago. They were bringing her back to Ando. I went and said the Mass. Her body is in the casket under the altar in Tia Maria's house. All I could find out was that she had not been well since Christmas. That must be why she never answered my letters. It seemed to be common knowledge there that it was the Maguirres who arranged to have the remains brought home to Ando. Some connection there; Esther was very mysterious about her father. I can say no more. It will take me a very long time to come to terms with my own grief; I am shattered ... Maggy and Raul had a baby at long last, a little girl. I hope it will help to bring them together. Such is life; one dies; another is born. It is hard to keep going and not be able to talk to anyone. I can only commend her to the good God in my poor prayers. Gugma ko, ngano ba intawon naglimbong ka?.

7.10.60 : I hear Mutt is away up the Amazon some place, where no white man ever went before. He is teaching the people a better way of planting their crops. We have another Kerryman here, a real sweetheart. He despises the Filipinos and makes no bones about it. Treats them the way farmers used to treat servant-boys, like dirt. A real Dan O'Connel type of a

Kerryman. "Keep the shaggers out", is his motto. It baffles all, why a man will go to so much trouble to save their souls when he can't stand the sight of them. He says they smell, a damn lie, for the poorest Filipino washes himself every day. Which is more than can be said of some whites who reek to high heaven. Filipinos find us most offensive when we dont wash; they have told me so because I took the trouble to ask .... I keep thinking of Esther; can't get her out of my mind. It was a hard lesson; brought me down to earth and back to my prayers. Changes may come, and I wouldn't bet on it, but it is a snare and a temptation to bank on the future. Maybe priests will be allowed to marry some day; maybe they wont. Meanwhile there is a job to do and God's grace is sufficient, if I do my part. He will not test us beyond our strength ... Tremendous interest in the American elections. Will Kennedy make it? He certainly beats Nixon hands down on looks. The women's vote could swing it as much as the civil rights.

7.1.61 : I am beginning to have second thoughts about much of the work we do here. The people see the church on the side of the rich and powerful. They cling to her coat-tails to get into heaven. We are told to keep out of their internal affairs and stick to the simple gospel. But Jesus preached justice; He wasn't afraid to speak His mind. None of the others seem to have a problem but I feel myself to be in what the Yanks call a catch-22 situation. Even if the council brings changes, they will take years to filter down this far. ... Kennedy made it by the skin of his teeth. The best part of it, for most of the Irish and Americans here, is that at long last we have managed to give the WASPS a black eye .... I often think of Esther and what might have been; she comes to me in my dreams sometimes. I will never forget her. Bessy, when I heard you were married, I think I set my heart on her, almost unbeknownst to myself. A bitter lesson; it is even harder now that the possibility of priests marrying is in the air. If it comes, it comes; I cant ever let this happen again; my own personal decision must be out of the way first, before any kind of close relationship is allowed to develop again. I wont

101

ever again let a woman get inside my guard till I'm free. I'd have it on my conscience but she's the one gets hurt.

2.2.61 : It is interesting to observe and to compare the people here with the Irish back home. One can walk into any house and sit down and talk; you get whatever they have. The same as on Goladuff. They tell me themselves that they find it hard to forgive an injury. I think they're honest; we only cod ourselves that we forgive from the heart. No one can forgive without the grace of God and we dont ask for it because we dont want to want to forgive. But they do suffer less than we do from guilt and anxiety and hang-ups; Filipinos never seem to worry about tomorrow. They are more natural, less particular about shame and false modesty, about bodily functions. They carry far less baggage. A squeamish Irish priest, answering nature's morning call, went to great care to secrete himself in the undergrowth, lest he be observed. But a skiff of rain started and his kind hostess, being concerned, sent an umbrella after him. He heard nothing as he squatted, but did notice that the shower had stopped. He looked up and there was the pretty daughter of his hostess holding the umbrella over him ... Bayut is a term that covers a wide spectrum of male effeminacy. He is the butt of numerous jokes, more tolerant and good-humoured than vicious. The priesthood has a peculiar attraction for bayuts, and they advance in the ranks because they are considered safe, rather than on their merits. I dont think the people believe that any priest, or any man for that matter, is truly celibate. A priest who has a wife sub rosa, is faithful to the one woman and takes great care of his children, often at great expense to the parish. The bishops differ among themselves about such men; some bishops sack them; some turn a blind eye, more concerned that the people can have Mass, and to prevent them from falling into superstitions and crazy beliefs. Strangely to our way of thinking, the people are inclined to trust the priest who has a woman, for the simple reason that his life is an open book to them; they're not inclined to trust the celibate because they suspect he has something on the side, somewhere. They have told me so, giving me that look, "Come on now, Padre".

25.2.61 : Fasting from midnight is no joke here; never gave it a thought in Ireland. Out here it's tough with the heat, to say 3 or sometimes 4 Masses of a Sunday and preach at them too and hear confessions and baptise. Without bite or sup one is like a wet rag by 1pm. Many of the older men have their stomachs ruined. It cant be right; surely a sip of water wouldn't break the fast .... The whole world loves Pope John; he's such a kindly soul, so human. Of course it's easy for me to like him; he confirms many of my own convictions. Thank God we lived to see the day when Pius X11's successor would say that God wants us to grow to full maturity as human beings. Surely God wants every Christian, man or woman, to have a free conscience, to stand on his or her own two feet before God. The old guard dont know whether to laugh or cry ... Who knows what all the ingredients are that go into the human animal to make him tick. There is free will; each choice we make bends us in a certain direction; our life's choices add up to who we are. Then there is God's grace, freely available but he likes us to ask. We have him who died on the cross for us, and his mother, and his church. What about the devil? The smart know-alls who know damn-all, tell us there is no devil. It suits old Satan fine to be a figment of the imagination; a poker-player loves the company of fools. Then we have the heritage in our genes, a potent brew, call it what you will. St. Paul blamed it all on our original parents, Adam and Eve; that's a bit simplistic; it's more like the sum total of all the sins of our fathers and mothers and all our ancestors, back along the line. We are all warped, bent, taking after our long line of forebears. The old penny catechism got it right though it explains it wrong; it is a force which 'darkens our understanding, weakens our will, and leaves in us a strong inclination to evil'. And we cannot suppress our feelings the way we were always told to do; they have a big say too, though they are as fickle as the weather; if we ignore them they turn round and bite us. But that's still not the whole story; there is the sum total, the residual grace of all the good deeds of all our fathers and mothers in our genes too. Have you never been surprised by the goodness of your own heart? Our beloved are not dead; they are alive in God; their love is working in us still, urging us to fight the good fight, to do the good to our brothers and sisters; to help every lame dog over the stile, flesh of my flesh; to do all for love and count it nothing. The Lord looked at the people with compassion, for they were like sheep without a shepherd .... I often think of Esther and what might have been.

3.3.61 : Saxon jokes and bawdy rhymes are a tradition among the clergy, with which they spice up the all-male conversation, and while away the lonely hours. Some are extremely witty; some pretty raunchy, some merely crude; some plain filthy. Nearly all are spawned by an unhealthy prurient fascination. Here is a pretty harmless old chestnut which came down to us from one of our betters and made the rounds, the brain-child of a very reverend monsignor and university president no less :

There was an oul sheikh from Rabat

Who pissed in the vizier's hat.

Said the vizier, "Oh hell, you may shit there as well?".

"I will", said the sheikh", and he shat.

I am no way squeamish, and I think I have a sense of humour, but I never cease to be amazed at the unctious front these same clerics are so careful to present to the layfolk. You'd think butter wouldn't melt in their mouths.

i.4.61. One can get hit by a phenomenon known as culture-shock when one goes to another country; so Time magazine informs me. We had a case in point here the other day. A little round bishop, a cultured gentleman, came to visit. We wined and dined him and danced attendance round him, as is only fitting, even for a Phil bishop. Besides, the Man himself said we ought to be as wise as serpents; we must take care to keep in a bishop's good graces if we hope to continue working in his diocese. Meal finished he paused for a moment in his discourse on the glories of church music, pushed himself away from the table, patted his ample midriff, belched mightily to show his appreciation for our hospitality and our cook Beato, and announced he was now ready for his siesta. We escorted him to his room. He put his hands on the table and bent over. Our superior Pauge, thinking his excellency was going to sit down, hastened to place a chair under the red-robed posterior. 'Muy bueno', says his lordship, releasing a prolonged fart that went from middle C to low E. Pauge was in the direct line of fire; one could tell it on his face. All the same he took the brunt of it manfully and never flinched. 'Deo gratias, for this relief much thanks', says the wee bishop, bowing us out, all the while smiling sweetly like any child of Adam you ever saw breaking wind. One is constantly bumping into Shakespeare round the oddest corners.

4.4.61: JFK dominates conversation here; Americans split along party lines, the Irish all for him. The father, Joe, was some operator. He made his son the president to get back at the Wasps in Boston who looked down on him, poor or rich, as shanty Irish. The Irish regard Kennedy's election as a triumph for the church, God giving us just revenge on our enemies.

8.4.61 : As I was saying the last time, I'm beginning to question aspects of our work here. The country is over 90% Catholic, at least in name. But they never got much choice. We baptise them and leave them without Mass or the sacraments. But for the legion of Mary, the vast majority of poor people would be completely on their own. They manage very well in the circumstances; have a great sense of God and prayer in their lives; they love Mother Mary. Close to nature; close to God. Most barrios have Mass only once a year, if that, at fiesta time. We are doing some good and mean well; no doubt of that. But we are only a stop-gap; after more than 50 years, we had to be forced, in the past couple of years, to accept native vocations. The church is not indigenous here after almost 400 years; can't supply it's own priests; largely the fault of us patronising foreigners. To most, this is almost blasphemous, but it is the truth .... We make no effort at official level to understand the culture, to know the history. We bring them all this baggage of our culture, our attitudes, our prejudices. Some Irish priests are teaching Africans to play hurley; we haven't gone that far; we have a few hurley-sticks here but strictly for our own use ... The Filipinos tell me that every Spaniard, the minute he set foot in the Philippines, was a grandee, blue-blood aristocracy; they'd walk on you. Most of them in fact were adventurers, a mixed bag, street-sweepers, no visible employment, jail-birds, back in Spain and Mexico. Many Irish priests I find are little better; the collar makes them aristocracy, even if they come from the bog. Some of them treat the natives like dirt ... I still haven't got over Esther; probably never will. It was a dream, a crazy dream, and she never knew. I can still hear that tinkling laugh.

17.6.61 : I was thinking; are the people in the barrios, who are not married, really living in adultery? Maybe it's not as big a deal in God's eyes as we make it. I am getting to understand the people a little better and I like them. They are genuine. This thing about delaying the wedding; the rules were relaxed during the Japanese occupation, because they very often couldn't get a priest and this has continued. Many Filipino priests, once they get out of the barrion, are not keen on going back; they often say they cant understand us going to the hardship of trekking through the mountains. But the real reason for putting off the wedding is that hospitality is so important to them that they can't have a wedding without a wedding-feast, when both extended families and the whole barrio has to be fed for days; a bit overboard by our standards, but that's their way. They can't afford it for the present, but please God, some day they will. In the meantime, who knows, maybe the white missioner will come and let them off the hook without losing face. For Big-nose takes no prisoners and he doesn't know or care about silly local customs like wedding-feasts. How can we lose face when Big-nose does the round-up, like in the cowboy movies?

11.8.61 : The church is compromised here. A few families own everything and the rest live hand-to-mouth. No middle-class. The clergy are seen to be on the side of the rich and powerful;

the hill folk cling onto the church's coat-tails to get into heaven. It's not too bad here, where the rural people have some freedom, but in the sugar lands for example, the people are no better than serfs of the landlord. The landlord helps the priest to build the chapel; so he owes him one, is under his thumb. We cannot even say Mass for the tenants without the landlord's permission. I wouldn't last long if I brought up land reform in the sermon. We are constantly warned by our superiors, not to get into their internal affairs; just preach to gospel and keep your nose clean. How can one preach the gospel and leave out justice? I'm beginning to feel in a cleft stick. There is a layman here by the name of Montemayor who knows his stuff and is not afraid to challenge the status quo. The bishops dont want him rocking the boat; the landlords call him a communist. He is risking his life. What's more, he comes from the landlord class, so his own family hate his guts. He is organising the sugar workers on the principle that there is strength in numbers.. Montemayor maintains that the right to private property is not absolute; that the workers by rights have a stake in the land they work. This is heresy by Catholic teaching today, but not according to the belief and practice of the early church. If I, as a foreigner, say 'boo', I'll be in hot water with the 'haves' and my own superiors.

24.9.61 : A group of well-educated, conscientious politicials have banded together to work for land reform; they call themselves the Grand Alliance party. They know their stuff, including the real Catholic doctrine. One morning during the election campaign, they stopped with us for breakfast. I was most impressed, especially by two senators, Pelaez and Manglapus. They know more about Michael Davitt and Gladstone and the Irish land acts than any Irishman; went to England and Ireland to study it in depth; using the Irish case as a model. They're trying to get Marcos to join them, but he and Imelda have their own agenda .... It is the custom here to commemorate a deceased person's birthday, not the anniversary of the death. A messenger came tó say that Mrs Maguirre wished me to come to Barongan. I was puzzled but curious; the boss said, "go"; no one says no to Donna Isabel. I was treated like royalty. The first of September was Esther's birthday; I said Mass for her in the private chapel. Tia Maria was there, wearing her black mantilla. Before leaving I was summoned into the presence of her ladyship and Tia Maria. "Esther's mother came to me and Esther herself told me about you, Father', she said, 'that she confided in you, and your kindness to her, and how you helped her. Now we have decided to take you into our confidence. Esther was my niece, the daughter of my brother-in-law", and she mentioned the name of a priest in the diocese. So that was why the Maguirres had brought her back to Ando. It also explained, among other things, why Esther had been peculiarly reticent about herself. Was that why she had said she would never marry, never have children?. But Donna Isabel was not yet finished,"Tia Maria feels there is something strange about Esther's death. She had not written from Christmas, which was totally unlike her". I promised to get in touch with my sister; they knew Esther had been staying with her. Come to think of it, Maggy had been very scant on details .... I wrote; Maggy's answer is vague; ignores my questions. It looks like something did happen. She just repeated what she had told me at the time, that Esther had died in her sleep. The baby was starting to talk, she said; she is expecting again; no mention at all of Raul.

31.12.61 : Fr Tom was a Maynoothman before he joined up; went to the PI in the early 30's and worked in the leper colony. The war caught him in Ireland; it was '46 before he got back to his beloved lepers. He was still with them when I first met him. He joins us here for dinner on big occasions. On Christmas Day he asked me to take his place with the lepers while he makes his private retreat on the first 10 days of January. Because we are from the same diocese he trusts me; I dont know why. So I'm off to the leper colony in the morning. Only one rule, he warned me, one can only get leprosy through physical contact .... Fr Tom would disagree with St. Peter; the only way to get him to agree to anything is by suggesting the opposite. We want him to take an odd break after all these years, so we remarked innocently that, with the cushy job he has, he didn't need a holiday. "I'll be on a plane one of these days", says he. But he'll never leave the lepers.

4.2.62 : My spell with the lepers was good for the soul; these are the least brethren. The disease can now be controlled, and in some cases cured, if it's got in time. That's the rub. The family has the same shame as an Irish family has if a member gets TB. It's a reflection on the family. They hide them; often it's too late. First sign is a coarseness of the skin and features; babies of leper mothers are born clean and they have to be separated. First to go are the extremities, fingers, toes, ears, nose. It is hard to look at some advanced cases. In tropical waters there is a jelly-fish called a man-o-war, huge, flaming-red, trailing long, multicoloured streamers; the sting can kill. I saw a girl in the hospital there. They told me she was eighteen; her face looked like a man-o-war, her two eyes swimming in a mass of red. Her husband was tending her. In my ignorance I remarked that it was hard on him. All he said was, "She is my wife". I felt small, rebuked by his love. Those four words spoke volumes; it taught me a lesson.

5.4.62 : Just got back from a place called Cagayan de Oro on the northern side of Mindanao, where I had an extraordinary experience. Here the Catholics are called Christians, as opposed to Moslems; they are mostly pioneers who have moved from the central islands, Leyte, Samar, Cebu, Negros, to break new ground. I followed the Cagayan river up into the mountains for three weeks, often wading where there was no path and no room for one. The river falls more than three thousand feet in the first thirty kilometres from the coast; just shows the hydro power available in most of the islands; it would have been child's play for the Americans to harness it; they did damn-all in their almost half-century here except talk big and steal the natural resources for Uncle Sam.... Spent three days as usual in each barrio; came to the last one. The people said that there were no Moslems in the area but that there were aborigines further up. The rainy season came early and I couldn't get back down; the river was suddenly one waterfall after another; I'd have to wait for the water to subside a bit. Not too exciting, cooped up, conversation limited; nothing to read; staring out at the rain day after day. On the fourth morning three men came up, Leytenos they said they were, from Maasin in Leyte, heading further into the interior with supplies. They could travel even in these conditions because they had a bull carabao with them. Leyte has the best carabao. The joke in the central and southern islands is that the only thing Leyte is good for is the carabao, and this fellow was as wide as a door. They explained proudly that he was five year old and that they had brought him from Leyte with them as a calf. Without him they wouldn't make it home for the gakid was gone. I wondered what the gakid was. The temptation was too much for me; on the spur of the moment I decided to go on with them. They said they were in touch with the aborigines. That clinched it. We set out, walking at first on a flat, open plateau until we could hear the river. A gash, not more than 200 yards wide, appeared in the plateau. We came to the edge; the river was roaring far below, could be a thousand feet down. Down we went by a tortuous path, step by step down the side of the gorge. The carabao is a study and a marvel in this kind of terrain; he takes his time; leans his huge bulk on his rump till he finds his footing, then inches forward. The safest place is on his back; it doesn't bother him; he never panics. At the bottom I could see a hemp cable slung over the deafening river, but the gakid or raft was gone. The three men stripped to the skin and I followed suit, and the clothes were stuffed in a US army canvas bag, which was tied on the carabao's neck between his horns. Then they loaded him up with the supplies, also wrapped in canvas. They offered me a lift on him too; there was still room, but I said if they were swimming so was I. The carabao walked straight across, no problem with all that weight on him, only his muzzle showing for air. The strength of the water carried us, though it wasn't more than four feet deep, and we landed 200 yards downstream, the three of them keeping on the lower side of me, just to be sure. We dressed in the rain; not easy; try it sometime. From there we followed a tributary. They took me home with them and fed me. They were cousins and had opened a small clearing in the forest and were growing rice and corn and vegetables, all in their mid-twenties. Two of them had wives still in their teens and one had a baby. I married them. They joked the bachelor; could I find him a woman on my travels? After a short rest, the bachelor came with me and we continued on up in the pouring rain and reached the aborigene huts before nightfall .... They are gentle people; wouldn't harm a fly; have fallen on hard times; their way of life is nearing it's end; the noose of civilisation's greed is strangling them. They are Stone Age people, racked with modern man's diseases. They had a prophet who attended a Christian school on the coast; he told them that if the soldiers' bullets killed him, not to worry; he would return. He got killed last year. Waiting for him to come back, they did not plant in the spring and are now half-starved, mal-nourished, surviving on fruit and berries. We shared the little we had with them. It was a real pity of the children. As far as I could make out, there were about sixty people all told in the village .... At night the shaman would chant for hours. My guide interpreted; said the shaman was honouring me as their guest shaman. It was a series of stories about the creation of the world and the flood, something like the account in the book of Genesis. It went on for hours. What struck me right away was that, in their version of things, God was a woman. I quizzed the guide on this to make sure and he was definite. I talked to the children, pointing to a boy - he, then a girl - she. Yes, no doubt about it, their God is a woman .... One story went something like this, 'The first man and woman lived in a beautiful garden full of trees, with every kind of fruit to eat, all except the tree in the middle of the garden. The good mother told them not to eat the fruit of that tree. because it was the poison-tree, the tree of death. But the bad witch stole into the garden and whispered in the man's ear and tempted him. He ate the deadly fruit, then handed it to his wife, who also ate, just to please her husband. The sleep of death came over them. The good mother came walking in the garden in the cool of the evening and found them dying and took pity on them. She touched the poison-tree. Suddenly it was weighed down with beautiful yellow fruit, hanging all over it like golden lamps. She took one, touched their lips with it and at once they were cured. Ever after it is called the mango tree, because it brought death and life .....

9.5.62 : Another gunk; I was hearing confessions last Saturday morning when a telegram was handed in to me through the curtain; "Come to Cebu to teach theology". So it's goodbye to the barrios. Our order, like most of them, refused to accept natives. Geromino was joined by a few lay-brothers after the war; not till '52 did we take a native vocation for the priest-hood, reluctantly, under duress, with a very bad grace. At long last a seminary is starting; the man ear-marked for theology has cried off injured, so Jeff is roped in at the eleventh hour. Things are in a state of flux with the council starting in October; a rous-ing time to be teaching theology out of a Latin textbook. If I keep a close eye on Pope John I cant go far astray. The shift from the mountains to the classroom reminds me of the executioner's song in the Mikado, 'a short, sharp shock'. I'd rather be up the Cagayan with the Leytenos and the aborigines; but haven't the courage of my convictions; not willing to pay the price. I wish I had Mutt's nerve to buck the system. I can see how it's easier for him; he's not complicated; is not tempted by the craving for a wife.

7.7.62 : We are almost ready to start the seminary. We have a great scripture man who studied for years in Jerusalem with scholars from the major Christian denominations, working on a new common bible to be published soon in French; he will be a big help to me in dogma. I will have 7 Filipinos and 4 Irish in my class and am teaching a Greek class and catechetics as well. Exciting; a challenge; two of the Irish are late vocations and will keep me on my toes. We will have discussion and debate in class; just follow the Latin textbook as a framework. No learning 6 pages of Latin by rote in my class. We will bring in the new theology; try to understand what is revelation, what is faith, what is the church, etc? I will make it clear to them that I am learning too; we are all searching for truth. What will come out of the council? .... Great stuff in the Time magazine on Kennedy and Nikita Khrushchev; the young fella is handling the oul bully like a Gene Tunney .... Esther is gone two years now.

15.8.62 : Met a Dutch bishop on the boat, on his way to the council. He has plenty of girls wanting to become nuns, in his diocese in Mindanao, but has no one to train them. Plans to visit Ireland, hoping to find a bishop who will give him three mature nuns. He is on the commission for the liturgy; told me he already has Mass in the vernacular, facing the people, for more than a year now. When I got back to base the community were at supper. I'm not exactly the silent type; "Latin is dead, buried, finito', I announced. Not for the first or last time Jeff was pronounced insane by one and all; how in God's name could the Mass be said in any language but Latin?

5.9.62 : Ando is far away now; couldn't get up there for her birthday Mass; wrote to Donna Isabel to explain my new situation to Tia Maria, and that I would say Mass for Esther on the day.

Chapter 8

8.10.62 : The big news is the Bay of Pigs fiasco. Kennedy walked into a haymaker; Khrushchev took that round .... The council has started. It will be interesting to see how die-hards like John Charles and Michael of Galway like the new climate, the fresh air sweeping through the church. Their medieval world is on it's ear. If you can believe Time, the Vatican thinks it's the end of the world, with the old man throwing windows open all over the place.. John just smiles and ambles away to have a chat with the plain folk .... Classes are going well; feeling my way. Most weekends I get away to the nearby barrios, or out to the leprosarium.

7.11.62 : We had a break at Hollontide and I got away to a sugar hacienda in Ormoc, owned by one of the big families, run by Ramon and Conception. He left Spain as a teenager and never went back; a tall, fairhaired Basque, getting on in years. She is from Mindanao, but is mostly of Spanish blood, dark hair, plump, vivacious, very devout, much younger than her husband. I hear her father had five daughters; guarded them with a shotgun. By all accounts, Conception hadn't much choice in the marriage. I stayed in the house with them and they made me feel like one of the family. She helped in the mission, teaching the children, etc. They take good care of their tenants, but are paternalistic. They dont pay too well but they keep the families together and support at least twice as many people on the hacienda as they need. The church is still in the driving-seat here and can make a good case against communism, intellectually and on the ground. The plain people love the church and are Catholic to the backbone. But it takes great courage and sacrifice to take the risk, and it's hard to change, and we humans are lazy and afraid of hardship, and of being labelled commies ourselves. A good sign - Montemayor, who is organising the poor farmers, has been invited to Rome as one of the lay participants in the council; as observers only but it's a start. The lay people used to take a full part in councils before Trent. That will give faint-hearts a bit of gumption. Montemayor is no man's fool; he got up to speak; the manners of a gentleman but no bowing and scraping. Only those with their ears open caught the subtle irony in his opening words,"Reverend Fathers of the Council, you sent for me; the Lord said 'Come and see', and I come". In other words, the Lord had offered an invitation; they had sent a summons. Maybe a tiny straw in the wind, auguring a change in the weather. The Council promises reform. Ecclasia semper est reformanda (the Church is in constand need of reform) is a very old adage, more honoured in the breach than in the observance. Most of the reformers got burned alive. Religion is notorious for causing blindness; if we could stand back and see straight, it should be obvious that the top-heavy set-up we have today is a perversion of the movement which Christ started. He came to unity humanity in the family of God, "that they may be one"; the only salvation is the love of God poured into our hearts to change us from hating to loving, if we let it soak in. Christ didn't set up a corporation; He said, "Love one another". Almost all the paraphenalia we have is man's handiwork, and has to do with power and polities and control. Will the axe be laid to the root? Frankly, I doubt it; one can only hope the Church will lose everything. Then we will be free. It took the Civil War to end human slavery in America. What will it take to bring reform in God's church?

8.12.62 : If you look at the map of the southern Philippines you will see strings and clumps of islands scattered in the Sulu Sea all the way down to Borneo. This is truly no-man's-land, a safe haven, a paradise, for pirates. They know no law; they have the latest weapons and high-powered boats. Monarchs of all they survey, they raid and prey on the southern islands at will. Any minute, any place, along the coast of Mindanao, they can hit like a thunder-clap out of a clear sky. They are not particular; they are efficient, using inside help or a hostage picked up on the way, as a guide. Why should they waste their time searching, when a local with a gun at his head can be their eyes and ears? They take only things of value but they do not usually kill or destroy, for they'll be back for more later. They're in no hurry, for they can easily outrun any vessel the government can throw at them. Choice prizes are girls to be sold as slaves. Twice so far I have been lucky; the pirates hit a coastal town where I happened to be. They struck and were gone and I didn't even know it.

28.1.63 : Slavery is still practised by the Moslems, that is, by those who can afford it. The Philippine government tolerates, recognises, their customs and laws because it cant do much about it. It can happen that a well-off Moslem will meet a Christian girl, at the university in Manila, for instance. They marry. He may even become a Catholic, for if she was brought up by the nuns, she wont have him otherwise. All is well till they move back to Mindanao; the minute his feet touch the ground, he is a Moslem again. In due course she is only one of several wives, depending on his pocket-book. If he tires of her, she becomes, for all practical purposes, a slave. If she runs away and is caught, she is pardoned the first time. If it happens more than once, her hamstrings are cut, the way they used to hough the cattle in the land troubles back home. That way she can still work but she cant run.

7.3.63 : The feast of St. Thomas Aquinas, the patron of seminaries. We are wrestling with faith and doubt in class. Thomas was a sound man for his time. Much is now laid at his door when the fault really lay with Trent for canonising the teachings of his commentators. I can see a lively debate coming up when we get round to transubstantiation, a true doctrine skewed by philosophers ploughing in where angels fear to tread. .... Ali Dimapuro is a Moslem senator in the national government, well into his sixties. He's a shrewd ecumenist; he has encouraged all his sons to marry Christian girls and his daughters to marry Moslems, because in our system the girl brings the dowry with her, and in the Moslem system the man brings it. So far it has worked according to plan; Ali got the money coming and going.

Recently his youngest son set his heart on a Moslem girl of sixteen. The custom is for father and son to visit the family of the girl, just like the match-making long ago in Ireland. When she let down her veil and Ali got a look at her, he told the son to go and find another lassy; he was taking her for himself. And he got the dowry too, being a senator. As they say here, the old volcano is not yet extinct.

24.4.63 : The council of Trent defined transubstantiation as an article of Catholic faith. This causes more difficulties than meet the eye at first glance; it brings in faith, revelation, the church, infallibilty. They're at it in the council and we're at it in class. I was explaining to them that Aquinas based his explanation of what happens at Mass on Aristotle's theory of material things being made up of substance and accidents. Who says so? It's only a theory and as such cant be defined as revealed truth. But Trent defined it. Where is the infallibility of Trent then? What does defining mean? Can revelation be encapsulated in a formula of words? Is faith to be found in a book, or in the head, or in the heart? Is doubt a sin? It is extremely interesting to hear the various comments. These young men from Ireland are light years ahead of us, in their freedom to question and to speak their minds. This is the new church in the making. Or is it? The Irish bishops led by their captain John Charles, with the Vatican in the full- back line, will take some moving.

3.5.63 : I asked the class to write an essay on any subject they liked, no holds barred. The results were interesting, apart altogether from the literary merits. Two of the Irish students played it cute, gave nothing away, which speaks volumes in itself. Wouldn't you know, both are from the South of Ireland. The late vocation, from Down, spoke his mind; said the Vatican was mostly to blame for the troubles in both Ireland and the Philippines. One Filipino said boldly that priests should side with the poor, that priests who wished to, should be allowed to marry, that women should be allowed to become priests. He ended his essay, 'I am proud to say that my grandfather was a priest'. Another Filipino wrote about the Manila galleon. Every year the Spaniards built a colossal floating warehouse in Manila Bay. They loaded it up with all the spices and Chinese silks they could beg, borrow or steal, and floated it with the trade winds to Mexico. Most years it made it, in spite of the Dutch and English pirates lurking along the sea-lanes like highway-men. When the galleon reached Acapulco, it's cargo payed for the administration of the Philippines in Mexican silver for another year. Then it was broken up for scrap. But before she had crossed the date-line, the building of next year's galleon had already started. Another Filipino wrote about the headhunters of Palawan. These are aborigines called Negritos, small and dark, similar to those I had visited in the interior of Mindanao, but, by this account, not nearly so peaceable. They hunt heads, not just for fun but with a purpose. When a young man's thoughts first turn to love, and he finds the maiden of his choice, he has to win her hand by bringing trophies to her father. Here is where things get complicated. Depending on her status, he has to come up with a certain number of human heads. So at a certain time each year, in the spring, hunting parties raid their enemies. If they come up short they're not too particular; any old head will do to make up the numbers. A foreign head is worth several native ones for the big nose. The interior of Palawan is not healthy in the springtime.

1.7.63 : Kennedy took Ireland by storm. That picture of him by the Berlin Wall at Checkpoint Charley, is the best answer to communism .... Pope John is gone home, his great work only begun. What a man! The church will never be the same again for we had a prophet among us. We can feel the effects of the thaw, an opening-up, God's warmth beginning to break through. Will the council fathers hold their nerve? We were discussing the Trinity in class, three Persons in one God, the deepest mystery of our faith. When we use the term 'person' today, we do not mean the same by it as the council of Chalcedon meant back in 385. That must give any serious person pause. If this is conceded, the way is open for recognising that dogma has evolved, and continues to evolve. The whole world loved John; may God have his great soul in His care.

13.8.63 : I was crossing Iligan bay on the ferry, the morning after that typhoon went up the east coast. The wind was still strong and the sea churning. I was out on deck and heard the look-out yelling, looked where he was pointing, then spotted something in the water up ahead. A bad time for sharks. It was an up-turned canoe with the people clinging to the out-riggers. A little closer and we could make out a man, a woman, a boy and a girl. In one hand the man held a gamecock high out of the water, keeping him dry for the fight. But every time a wave hit the out-rigger the cock got splashed; he did'nt like it one bit, shook himself and spluttered and crowed in fury. The ferry came around up into the wind. First to be rescued was the cock, then the man, then the boy, then the girl, then the wife. We had a lively discussion about it, when I brought it up in class. Did this pecking order come from native culture, or the Spaniards, or the Americans, or the Catholic church? I wish the council fathers had seen it; it would give them something to think about. Have they invited any women to the council?

1.10.63 : I was hoping that Cardinal Montini would not be chosen as the new pope. He has taken the name Paul V1. No one envies him trying to fill John's shoes. I must admit I am prejudiced against Paul; he was Pius X11's right-hand-man. By all accounts the aristocatic Pius treated him with barely con-cealed contempt as a mere cipher, a gofor. I fear for the future; Paul hasn't the strength of mind of John and will give in to the old guard. We'll have to wait and see, and hope. The straws in the wind dont look good. If only John had lived two more years; God's ways are surely strange.

23.11.63 : Hearing confessions on an empty stomach at 6 am in the tropics is no joke. During the rush hours at peak periods it can be up to 11 hours in the box, at a stretch, with an odd break for air. It's not what one hears that's the trouble; that's pretty harmless. It's mostly the old women in brown Franciscan habits we call the Antonianas, the salt of the earth, God bless them. They couldn't commit a serious sin if they tried. Their piety may be simple but it's genuine; I cant stand piety divorced from ordinary life, which seems to be largely our stock-in-trade here. The trouble with hearing their confessions is that these old ladies smoke the pure tobacco leaf, their beloved tustus, with the lit end inside the mouth. Worse still, the breath wafting through the slide on the morning air is heavy-laced with garlic. You could cut the air with a knife. Exactly at seven I came up for a breather. Rapid steps clattered up the aisle and I caught the ghostly whisper, "Kennedy was killed in Dallas". We know Camelot was but a dream; how can we live without our dreams?

Items discussed: Revelation did not end with the apostles. God speaks every day and at night too. We wont hear him if we dont turn off the noise......Piety by itself is only superstition...follow you conscience, come hell or high water.

20.12.63 : Christmas always brings thoughts of home and a stab of lonesomeness. The priest ploughs the lone furrow. I found myself back in the bakery, a safe haven of warm smells to escape to out of the dark, dank night. Terry was showing off his new hob-nail boots with their lovely diamond studs. Buddy the baker had wet the tay and was slapping on slabs of butter on hunks of toast, compliments of the house. The talk lapsed as we fell to. Terry's jaw worked in silent concentration, as he put down a foundation for a few pints and admired the boots. "Be Jasus", says he of a sudden and his eyes lit up, "no better man", and he took into greasing the boots with butter-paper. But the tale ended in sorrow; the rats et the brand new boots, and left nothing but the brass eye-holes and the shiny diamond studs.

6.1.64 : What is going to happen, now that John is gone? I was afraid of this; already Paul has started interfering with the council. I can see what's happening; the Vatican is putting pressure on him and he hasn't the gumption to stand up to them. John would smile at them and continue on his merry way. He infuriated the beaurocrats. He took them on the hop. They say the Vatican brass swore a mighty oath, 'After John, never again';

never again would they be caught napping. The trouble is that Paul has been a Vatican career person all his life, even though Pius sent him to Milan to get rid of him. The bloom is gone off the rosy-fingured dawn already.

27.3.64 : What few noticed about John was his strength, rooted in his trust in God; he did his little bit and didn't worry. Reform was internal; the work of the Spirit. John had the true faith. Paul's weakness is that he doesn't trust the Holy Ghost. He is a Pelagian. His face and his whole demeanour show that he is a worrier, carrying the world on his shoulders, caught between the old and the new. One day he agrees with the council; the next he goes back on his word. For him reform is external; he's trying to do the impossible, to reconcile Papal monarchy with episcopal collegiality. Here he goes gallivanting off to the Holy Land. It makes a big splash in the media, but what real good does it do? It's the legalistic, negative way the church is run that is the problem. Frankly, I am discouraged already, but have not let the class see it, I hope. It's tough when a dream is shattered. I can see it all already; Paul vacillates; the Vatican uses him; the work of the council is stymied; end of story. I did say to the class that we, as committed Christians, have a bounden duty to criticise, to contrast and compare popes in the light of the gospel. The all-too-brief golden age of John proves that the pope is the key to any real reform; it must come from the top down and meet the cravings of peoples' hearts.

15.4.64 : I got a letter from Maggy. She is worried about her health; Raul hasn't changed; and there is something else in her letter that I just couldn't put my finger on. Something is bothering Maggy; I think she thinks she has cancer and her conscience seems troubled. She says, "something I should have told a priest years ago ....". How does one answer a letter like that?

11.5.64 : Mighty discussions in class on what the council has come out with so far. The doctrine has been there all the time, but static; now a new emphasis, more dynamic; not so much having the facts in the head as putting the faith into practice. The faith is not in the dead letter; it is living in the heart. It goes far beyond the visible framework of the church, as in the civil rights for blacks, ala Martin Luther King. Why did the church not condemn Truman and his henchmen for dropping the bomb on Japan; the worst crime in human history, far worse than Hitler, who was a madman. Was Truman mad? What would have been the Vatican reaction if, instead of the bomb, the US had showered Japan with condoms? The Us government works hand-in-glove with big business to rob the PI of it's natural resources; the few bits of road in the islands were built to facilitate the rape of the country. The church has said damn-all about it. Montemayor was trying to help the poor farmers and not one bishop would let him into his diocese; he was called to the council and suddenly they all wanted him. I hope the change of heart is more than skin-deep. The Vatican has traditionally taken sides in wars; fomented the crusades; it's time to condemn all war; note, only males make war; they love killing. Not too long ago the Pope and many of the cardinals had slaves of their own. Pius 1X condemned the idea of freedom of conscience, less than 100 years ago. Our society treats women as inferior beings, little better than serfs, and the church has made no comment. And on and on, practices that cannot be reconciled with the words or actions of Christ. We must face the music, sooner or later; I fear the golden opportunity of the council has been missed; little more than window-dressing. We have been heavy-handed on the personal sins of the rank-and-file; mute on institutional, corporate vice, including our own.

7.7.64 : The Irishmen in the class were saying that the numbers in the Sem back home are away down. Amazing; down from 100 to less than 50 in the last 7 years. What factors made so many enter in the late 40s and early 50s; what factors have suddenly changed people's minds? It's not just materialism, or the new theology. It's a bit of a mystery. It makes one wonder how much of a real say we had in the decision; I honestly thought I did it completely off my own bat; obviously not. What makes the phenomenon so fascinating is that the sudden change of gears came before John and the council; even before the new theology had even begun to filter down to the ordinary people. There is already talk of selling the Sem in Galway and moving the remaining students to Dublin.

3.7.64 : I answered Maggy's letter as best I could. She wrote back; she thinks she has cancer, which I feared. The post-script was the bombshell, "Esther had a baby". That's all. I could see she had opened the envelope again and stuck in that last bit at the last minute. My first thought is, "If this gets out, I'm ruined; they'll surely say I was the father". Poor Esher, what a way to go. Did the baby survive? Was it a boy or a girl?

7.3.65 : Pope Paul continues to interfere with the council; he has taken several matters away from them. By what right? Obviously we are back with Pius and his idea that the Pope is above the council and the bishops and the church, rather than being part of it .... St. Paul put St. Peter in his box. Women wont get far in the church under Paul .... We were discussing in class how the council of Nicaea in 325 defined the doctrine of the Trinity, three persons in one God. A person originally meant the huge mask which the Greek tragic actors used; it acted as a kind of megaphone in the open-air amphitheatre. Later it came to mean an aspect of a human being. In other words, 'person' today does not mean exactly the same as it meant in 325. What word would more accurately convey the concept of the Trinity today? .... No further word from Maggy. I'll be going home in June and will go by Toronto to see her. With God's help she'll get better; the children need her. When I talk to her, face to face, I'll get all she knows about Esther out of her.

10.4.65 : Maggy has cancer, I'm afraid, from what she writes; I think she knows it. Raul gave her a dog's life. What will happen to the children? If she dies she will take her secret with her. I wont be able to go home until next year now; Johnson is sending the troops into Vietnam in numbers and they need chaplains, and I got my orders just like the rest of the buck-privates, the grunts, what the Greeks called the hoplites. They dont need me to teach here after June. The first chance I get before I check in at Subic Bay, I'm going to Samar to talk to Donna Isabel and

Tia Maria, to see if they know anything about the mystery of Esther's baby.

5.5.65 : I finally got away. The Maguirres are expecting me and Tia Maria will be there too. They have no idea why I'm coming. Crossing to Ormoc it was about midnight and I was lying on the bed, dozing. Most of the people were sleeping; a few still murmuring quietly. Ever so gently my watch was moving down my wrist. "Ayaw", I said, not moving a muscle. The thief stole away in the night. Just then someone came and sat down heavily on the empty bed beside me and heaved a sigh. Then the gasp, "Sus Maria, mi padre ". It was Concepcion. We spent the rest of the night talking. Ramon had at long last gone back to Spain to see his aging mother one last time. In Mexico, on the way back, he had suffered a heart attack and died. He was 62; she was my age, 35. She had a good foreman and still continued to run the hacienda. She was loyal to Ramon but I could see he had been a cold fish. She didn't know it or would-n't admit it to herself, but she is just like me, emotionally stunt-ed. Birds of a feather we are. Gradually we opened up to each other. It felt good to let my hair down for once. I told her all about Esther and my shattered dreams. As we sat there on camp-beds on the little steamer on the tranquil inland sea, I realised that this was only the second human being I had really talked to; for her it was probably the first; and we are are 35. Ah dear me. She had her two children to see through college. She would not marry again. I would be sure to come and visit her. And I thought, 'Wouldn't it be great to have a friend like this? But it cannot be. It might be as innocent as the babe unborn but people would suspect the worst. Another thing, knowing human nature, it would be bound to grow into something more. A woman who tangles with a priest is sure to get burnt when he ups and walks away. I promised to call in at the hacienda on the way back.

6.5.65 : Tia Maria was there. She and Donna Isabel listened quietly to what I had to say. If they were surprised they didn't show it; perhaps they know something I didn't. Donna Isabel will have someone check discreetly in Toronto and keep me informed. She was practical; if the baby had died, that was that. If it had lived, it would now be going on six. The first thing was to find it. If it could be done, she would do it. They both recognised the delicate position I was in; the foreigners are not as understanding as the Filipinos in such matters. Who the father might be was not discussed. If it was an accident, they could understand; if somone had taken advantage of Esther; he would pay. Asked a few questions of my own around Barongan; Raul's father gambled away everything on gamecocks; the Maguirres got their place .... I am now an official chaplain with the U.S. Army, Fourth Cavalry. Not too happy about having anything to do with this war, or any war for that matter. So far I have not had to go into Vietnam. War is hell, solves nothing, especially this one. Mostly the young, the poor and the blacks being brainwashed to turn out mindless killing-machines. Reminds me of young lads waiting for the rats at a thrashing. It is wrong to treat people like vermin. Glorification of war is a crime against humanity. It is also the height of stupidity to try to fight a holding war in rice paddies and jungle similar to the PI; catch 22 situation; one doesn't have to be a military genius to see that.. Most of the officers I have talked to, say so privately. I met a young fellow from Mayo; talks Irish; was only a few months in the States when he got called up. He's not too keen on the idea. I am shocked at the bigotry of Irish Catholics against the negroes. Nigger is one of the more polite names they call them. One of the MPs (military police) brags that he went to school to the Jesuits; he's a vitriolic s.o.b.; blames the effin niggers for all his troubles. He cant see, or wont see, that the white man brought them over as slaves only a few generations back. Bigotry is a disease .... They brought the Mayo boy back today in a bag .... I didn't keep my promise; never went back to visit Concepcion on the hacienda in Ormoc, though she needed me. I was afraid of getting hooked. A great pity; I need a friend like her, a kind, virtuous woman; her beauty frightened me.

6.6.65 : The church has wobbled a good few times, but has always come back to the true line. We have always been sound on the doctrine, often weak in the performance, slow with the mea culpa. It is of interest to note that the councils, on the whole, have been more consistent vehicles of the magisterium than have the popes. From Pius 1X to Pius X11, the Pope put himself above council and church; if you're above, you're outside. John and this council got us back on track, but Paul is already lapsing back into authocracy. I could only throw up my hands in horror when he took the birth-control issue away from the council. It augers ill. Abortion is wrong; but contraception, if not abortive, cannot be proved wrong from revelation. Who says it's artificial? What does artificial mean? Why should it be wrong because it's artificial? I can see I'm going to have a serious problem hearing confessions if this trend continues, if this is imposed on us as Catholic doctrine .... Donna Isabel wrote. Esther had a baby girl. They think she survived. But where is she? .... I better face it; priests will not be allowed to marry in my lifetime. If I was holier, if I was a man of prayer, if we had never got our hopes up, I might make it, maybe, with God's help. The fact is, I am the marrying kind. Now I'm slowly approaching a catch-22 situation myself. It's hard to stay and it's even harder to leave. It's starting to tear me apart. I can see the cross-roads looming ahead. Will I stay for the cushy life and the status, or face out into the cold, a nobody, when the crunch comes. For what can be lower on the totem-pole than the spoiled priest? As long as I could convince myself that this sacrifice was demanded by God, I could hack it. It has slowly dawned on me, during these years of teaching, that God asks this sacrifice of those only to whom He gives the special grace to be able to live a single life. We are not all called to be monks. I know my conscience is free, but a little voice whispers in my gut, "Judas". Oh the sins of the fathers and the mothers, how they link us into the force of evil. The battle is fought out in every life, the battle of the cross, Christ versus Satan, love versus possession .... One of the priests here is from Artane. He tells me the word back home is that that canatt Haughey is buying up land in north Dublin, near the airport, which is going to expand.

2.8.65 : Many Moslems in Mindanao send their children to Catholic schools. Some schools have more Moslem than Christian students. We Irish are not always sensitive to others' feelings; for example, in eastern cultures generally, it is reckoned worse for a male to lose face than to die. We find that hard to believe but it is true, as people have discovered too late. We had a tragic incident recently. A young, typical jackeen arrived, still wet behind the ears, but a loud-mouth know-it-all. Some of the older men tried to warn him but he listened to nobody. Whoever decided to send this abrasive character into the lions' den must shoulder the blame for what happened. The school day starts with the raising of the flag ceremony, following American custom. A Moslem youth sauntered in late and Fr. X yelled at him in front of the whole school. The boy turned and walked away, seemingly impervious to the mortal insults still being hurled at him from the stage. During the singing of the national anthem he reappeared, accompanied by his older brother, who calmly pumped six shots into the priest. The pair then walked away. They were tried under Moslem law and acquitted on the grounds of provocation .... A logging truck will sometimes kill a pig; the company must pay damages. If the truck kills a child, the damages are higher, but still only a fraction of the price of a truck. Some years ago, a truck killed a child and the company tried to be smart; they refused to pay up and moved the driver to another area. When six years had passed they thought it was safe to put him back on his old run. The very first trip, he was killed, and the truck set on fire. No shortcuts here.

Christmas, 65 : It's hard to keep going; it's easy to blame others for our troubles. I have to paddle my own canoe. As long as the powers that be in the church were making a genuine effort for truth, all along the line, as long as they were applying Christ's justice consistently, I could believe in what I'm doing and give it my best shot. The council has failed. The wonderful theory has been shelved. The vast majority of us priests are decent men who try to do our best. But I'm damned if I'm going to toe a party line that makes a mockery of the cross of Christ. Big business is devastating God's good earth and grinding the faces of the poor. The US government, under the thumb of big business, is laying waste Vietnam, perverting it's own youth into monsters and slaughtering the innocent, in an unjust, idealogical war, and I am a chaplain in the pay of Uncle Sam. But am I being honest? Am I looking for an excuse? The name 'original sin', and it's biblical explanation, may be inadequate; but anyone who denies the fact that humankind is sadly out of kilter is a fool. Which is better, to resign and go into private life, or to keep muddling along? I am one mixed-up kid of thirty-five .... Where is Esther's girl?

7.1.66 : I am sick to death of this Vietnam job. I have seen terrible things in the PI; the seal of confession prevents me from going into detail on paper, what goes on in this numbers game is hell. The leader of the free world, the champion of liberty, is trampling with caterpillar tracks over living bodies, and twisting minds into monsters. Men, women and children who haven't a clue what it's all about, poisoned, blown apart in the trees, floating bloated in the rice paddies. Civilised young men who shower every day, torch villages for fun. All for the almighty dollar and for mindless fear of the boogieman. God help us all. The human male's solution for every problem since the beginning is kill, kill, kill. Now we do it with style and an arrogant swagger. This is no primitive black man's spear job; the red man merely scalped his enemy with a crude tomahawk; this is modern, sophisticated war. White America's destiny is to bring democracy and civilisation to the whole human race. America, America, God shed His grace on thee .... And we bless them on their merry way and ask the Prince of Peace to give them the victory. What was that He told us we should be shouting from the roof-tops? Let me out.

4.2.66 : I have become very fond of the Philippines and it's mixture of peoples. It is an archipelago, a big word for a cluster of islands, stretching from near China in the north down toward Malaya in the south. The further north, the more Chinese blood in the blend; the further south the more Malayan. Add a dollop of Spanish here and there; a pinch of Americano, a little Indian. Only the higher classes intermarry, but that didn't stop the aristocracy from leaving their hallmark on many a face. Seven major languages are spoken and about a hundred and fifty dialects, all Malayan. Variations in speech are separated, not by the seas between the islands, but by the mountains. It seems they had these variations before they came from various parts of Malaya and Indonesia, at different times. By a wierd fluke the definite article is 'an', the same as in Irish. Their musical talent and their sense of humour bring them close to us. This past year they celebrated four hundred years as Catholics; Rome has canonised hundreds of Europeans and thousands of Italians, but hasn't yet got round to giving them even one saint, not even a blessed. Your ordinary, everyday Filipino would knock spots off most Italians for living the Christian life. Especially the women. I have had the great privilege of knowing many women here who are living saints; and some men too. I sometimes think I could do a whole lot worse than settle here. An American by the name of McCaffrey took the plunge a few months ago, and has settled in Mindanao. The jeep pulled up one morning, with the wife and mother-in-law and all their worldly goods. He said Mass; then the wedding party joined us for breakfast. He is no oil painting but he has good taste; I'm not so sure about the mother-in-law. I truly envied him the way he escaped from the toils of our prejudices and conventions, like the bird from the fowlers' snare, 'ex laquio venantium'. He will continue to minister, no questions asked. I have often dreamed of Ando; Esther is always in the dream and she's gone.

14.3.66 : Donna Isabel's secret service have been doing some digging. The trail is getting warm. At the time of Esther's death, it was suspected that she had had an abortion which went wrong. The death certificate says 'natural causes'; probably a quack signed it for a price. The wake was in Raul and Maggy's house. Had she died there? Where did the baby disappear to? They think Esther's girl lives somewhere in Toronto, not in an orphanage but with a family. Illegal aliens dont keep records. Naturally Tia Maria would like to see her grandchild. Donna Maria will leave no stone unturned, spare no expense, until she is found. Surely Maggy knows what happened; something has been bothering her conscience since she got sick; the weight on her conscience cant be helping her health .... I just mailed a letter to Maggy, telling her what we know, asking her to tell us the truth; Donna Isabel will spare no expense .... I'm heading for Ireland in June; it's about time. Dad died in '61 and I couldn't get home to see him one last time, not even for the funeral. I have to see my mother Ketty before it is too late. We dont know the day nor the hour.

29.4.66 : Maggy wrote back; out came the whole story; it was staring us in the face all the time and we couldn't see it. Maggy's eldest is in actual fact Esther's girl. Maggy had waited so long for a child of her own; it seemed God had sent the baby; she couldn't resist. She swears not a soul knows only Raul. Esther's baby is now almost six; her name is Teresa, Terry for short. .... I just got off the phone with Donna Isabel. We agreed, let the hare sit. She is arranging for a bank account for Terry in Maggy's name. Arrangements are to be made for her to visit 'granny' in Ireland in the summer and 'granny' in the Philippines at Christmas. I think Terry should be told the truth, sooner rather than later. Has Maggy told her anything yet? Does Maggy know, or rather, guess, who the father is? Maybe Esther told her.

24.5.66 : I am sick to death of this nightly farce. The newsmen sit in the Hotel Saigon drinking whiskey; being briefed every evening by the army; sending this crap to the American public, knowing full well it's a complete fabrication of lies. One word of the truth and no more whiskey, no more job. You tell the truth, you disappear, sometimes literally. I cant hear the soldiers' confessions; their consciences are coming alive and they are in bad faith if they stay. They must refuse to obey and damn the consequences, even the disgrace of courtmartial. It's a tough one; each man must make his own moral choice. I'll be back on Goladuff in a fortnight after eight years, to spend a little time with my mother, and to catch my first glance of Esther's child. What of the future? My own moral choice is looming ever closer.

15.6.66 : Back on Goladuff with mother in the old place with the empty chair. The little familiar things, water slapping a cot, water-fowl calling, moss on a stone, the house-leek on the gable; thinking to myself, 'I shoulda never left home'. The water of the lough is calm, but already I hear Paisley and the Devlin girl rumbling, like coming thunder. Terry and I hit it off from the word go. She has red hair and Esther's eyes. She is wise beyond her years; I'm tempted to tell her but dare not. Better leave well enough alone; she need never know she's adopted.

8.8.66 : Ma, little Terry and I had a wonderful time, just the three of us on lovely Lough Erne and her islands so green. For a brief moment all the years were a dream and there was only the water reflecting the sky and the shadowy trees and the rim of the low hills. Promised to take Terry down to Clifden; plans cut short by a call from headquarters. Maybe just as well to leave well enough alone. I'll have to get out of this sorry chaplaincy business. It's no better than aiding and abetting murder; I have blood on my hands but I'm under orders. They tell me I cant get out of the contract until January. I'm torn in two about giving up the priesthood altogether; one day leaving, the next staying. If I stay I'll have to live with my cowardice. If I go I'll have to live with my guilt. I'll have to live with myself either way .... Terry breaks my heart; I wish I could throw my arms around her and never let her go. What is best for her, that's the rub. She appears happy enough, but who knows what goes on inside that serious little girl's head? I know she likes Ireland and will love Ando a lot more than Toronto, but what can I do?

I wont see her any more; it's better for both of us. She could have been my daughter.

1.9.66 : I hear mighty stories about Mutt. Ever since he escaped from Rome he has been up the Amazon; never went home. You remember the Kerryman here who's motto was,'Keep the shaggers out'. Well, they recalled him and made him a bishop and sent him off to Brazil. As luck would have it, Mutt ended up under your man, and naturally, being two Kerrymen, they fell out. Mutt headed for the hills and his lordship promptly excommunicated him; what else was he in power for? Mutt lost no sleep over it and continued his work of teaching the villages to farm the Kerry way; he was always keen on the parable about the 'sower who went out to sow the seed'. He was now technically within the ambit of an American bishop. One day this long-headed monk appeared on the innocent man's doorstep; he wanted money to build a chapel. He got the loot and disappeared back into the jungle. When the bishop got back from the last session of the council he discovered that Mutt had built a road instead of a chapel.

11.11.66 : This war is diabolical. We're on a carrier somewhere in the South China Sea, lobbing death into the population, like Ted Williams shagging baseballs, pounding the living daylights out of the good earth and every living thing on it into pulp. Americans are geniuses at technology. Unfortunately, they also breed the blinkered specialist with the tunnel vision, the perfectly sane madman, a dangerous mutant. Hence napalm is pure logic; soak the trees, soil, animals, humans, all life, with poison gas and light it. What would a man do if his field was infested with rats? What else only spray the living daylights out of the fuckers? In the time-honoured tradition of General Phil Sheridan, that heartless bigot from Killinkere, who thought up the dandy plan of exterminating the Plains Indians without risking the white man's neck. Simple; he killed off the buffalo and the white man got a bounty and the Indians, men, women and children, starved to death. The big tankers drone in from the Philippines and dump the stuff by the ton. And these are the saviours of the world, the same self-righteous craw-thumpers who dropped the bomb on Japan, and hung Hitler's gang at Nuremberg for genocide. Into the bargain, it is totally logical to pervert the minds of young blacks and white trash, to do your dirty work for you for patriotism. God bless America, dulce et decorum est pro patria mori, and all that crap. .... Mutt was always a born bachelor. It never dawned on him that women were different; he didn't notice them. Wee Jeff's antennae picked up vibes like a martian. He would walk into a room and, without even looking, knew instantly who was the best-looking woman there. He'd glance across at Mutt, the long head the shape of a pointed egg, the point to the back like a bike helmet, the face as remote as a eunuch's on a mummy's tomb, and envy him his happy state ..... Terry is coming to Tia Maria for Christmas. I'd love to see her, but I think it's better for both of us, in the circumstances, if I dont show up.

15.1.67 : Thank God, I'm free of the mayhem and back in Mindanao. Most of the parishes here are run by Irishmen. The older men were thrown out of China by the commies. These are the true professionals; they man the parishes, living on their own at the back of beyond year in year out. We are only in the haypenny place in comparison. Every so often we all get together on a Sunday evening with the bishop, for a meal and a couple of beers and a chat. Afterwards, some of us play a little poker; others bridge. It's usually 2am when we break up. We head for bed in our big monastery; each of them sets out in his jeep for some distant outpost. Great men, in anybody's book. Last Sunday night we had a mighty discussion about the changes coming in the church. An old veteran of China said nothing all night. When all the talking was done he got up and stretched himself and spoke for the first time, "The youngest man here will see no real change in his lifetime. Old ways die hard. The Vatican will not move till it's brought to it's knees'. It had the ring of prophecy to it. We went our separate ways cold sober .... They tell me our gardener went to prison for killing a man.

28.2.67 : Maggy wrote. Her health is much better. I'm sure getting that burden off her conscience was a big help. She says Terry enjoyed visiting her two grannies; is looking forward already to summer and Christmas. She is coming out of herself a bit. Often asks about me .... I heard a good one recently about Mutt. He was saying Mass in a village chapel. It seems two political prisoners had escaped in the next state, had made it over the state line and were in the congregation. Their pursuers surrounded the chapel and, being pious Catholics, waited for the Mass to finish before moving in. Mutt was pouring in the wine and water and spilled the water all over himself. He had to send an altar-boy for more water. After the last blessing the ringleader of the posse called out that they had the place sur-rounded and to send out the wanted men. Mutt said, "Look behind you". At a number of vantage points stood men with rifles, surrounding the posse. Mutt had sent a message with the altar-boy who went for the water. In a culture where the women do most of the praying, all the men were not at Mass. "It's an ill wind", said Mutt to himself .... I am still wrestling with the angel. Am I honest when I tell myself that I am called to the priesthood, but not to the single life? Am I trying to make a case for doing what I want to do?

4.4.67 : I like the work here in Mindanao, in the barrios close to the common people. I feel at home, one of themselves. Every now and then we Irishmen get together for a breather, when all the Masses are finished on a Sunday evening. Some of us say five Masses because of the need; canon law allows only three, so we're stretching it a bit. We share a meal and a chat; some take off for the pictures in the flea-bitten cinema; some play poker; the bishop himself likes to join us for a couple of rubbers of bridge when he can. Then there is Dick; he joins in nothing, fear ann fein but a man of many parts, a veteran of China and the Japanese prison camps. Dick very rarely dines at home where the cupboard is bare; only ice in Dick's icebox. He eats twice a week, usually managing to hit a fiesta or a wedding or a chris-tening, or at worst, a funeral. Now he's muy contento, full to the gunnel, sauntering around the sala, patting his ample midriff, sucking on a bottle of San Miguel, smacking his lips. He annoys some of us when he kibitzes over our shoulders at the cards, "For God's sake Dick, willya take yourself off and make us a limerick". "Gimme a hint". "How about the tooth you got out yesterday?". By the end of the hand Dick is back with his masterpiece -

> There was a young lady called Quilling
> Who went to the dentist for drilling
> But due to depravity he filled the wrong cavity
> Miss Quilling's now nursing her filling.

7.5.67 : I am something of a loner like Dick. So it was welcome news when the new assignments came; I'll be completely on my own for the first time. In January I go as chaplain to a sugar refinery; to be the resident priest for the workers and their families, about 4000; the hacienderos and their families come to Mass too, sometimes. It's very up-to-date, with sewage, electricity and a hospital. The population explosion is blamed on lack of rural electrification; on the other hand, the world is really divided between those who have a jacks and those who have none. I have visited there twice and have a good idea of the job. Will have my own house with housekeeper, a motorbike and a modest salary, thanks to the Tabacalera Company. This postpones the evil day of dire decision, at least for a while. I'll be in the territorial parish but outside the range of the famous Fr Roca, the man with the gun. Even the bishop gives him a wide berth; no curate will stay with him. Nobody knows for sure but they estimate that he has 40,000 in his parish, every last one of them Catholics, and he's all on his ownio and not getting any younger. No false prophet would be foolhardy enough to pitch his tent in Roca's domain. They say the last time it was tried, his reverence preached a warning, that lightning would strike. They ignored him. Then somebody spilled a little gasoline in the dark and happened to strike a match. Fr. Roca made sure they got out safe; gave them a good breakfast and put them on the first bus out. The next Sunday the theme of his sermon was,'I told you so'. The one time I met him we got on swimmingly but I'll have to be on my toes and keep a weather eye out .... St. Paul's 'sting of the flesh', one would expect it to subside as one gets older; instead it's worse; a persistent nagging, like an itch. Others seem immune; how do they manage it? Maybe they are like the people who live on top of the San Andreas Fault and never give it a thought. The physical urge never leaves me, like a craving for forbidden fruit. I was thinking that we who joined up in such droves after the war had our personal motives; but were we actually helpless in the grip of unknown forces? The sudden drop in numbers would seem to say so. Similarly, numerous reasons have been advanced at different times for and against celibacy. What about the blind, primordial drive of the species? Can that be snaffled without dire consequences? What do I know, but I cant help thinking .... Maggy's health is keeping good, thank God. Terry is doing well in school. Who was her father has not come up .... Dick is a Dublinman who's father had a pub; he was telling about an argument between a Kerryman and a Cavanman, which hoor was the cutest. "We need a drink", says the Cavanman. "Lukkat John B. Keane", says the Kerryman. "True for you", says the Cavanman, "Who's buyin?".

12.5.67 : Geronimo has arrived so it's like old times again. He's a mine of information about Imelda. She is the power behind Ferdinand; is pushing him; wants to be Mrs. President. Is going the right was about it; has her children boarding with the Irish nuns; is courting the bishops. We have our first cardinal; they say she pulled strings to get the red hat for Rosie. Geronimo remembers her barefoot. Her very first pair of shoes were baklas, wooden clogs; the way she hit the boardwalk with them told you she was going places even then; tall for five, she stood out, with her haughty good looks and fierce drive ... I was asking Geronimo about a couple of things that puzzle me. One, why have I never seen a girl playing a guitar here? He looked at me as if I wasn't right in the head, "Who would do the work?". Number too, I have never seen anyone barefooted, because of the schistosomiasis, but he said Imelda was running around in her bare feet as a little girl. Geronimo explained, "The Japs brought the schisto; they ate snails; the schisto bug lives in the snail. Never put your foot on the bare ground. If it gets in, it heads for the brain. Tapus na; you're finished" .... Our gardener was back cutting the grass this morning. He got a year but they let him out after seven months for good behaviour. I asked Geronimo how come he got off so light? "A good-for-nothing started pestering his wife when he got him away working. The gardener warned him twice outside the tuba-house, where he was playing majong and drinking with his cronies. The fellow made fun of him and kept on making a nuisance of himself. The third time, the gardener put his bolo in his basket when the day's work was done, put the basket on his head and walked slowly to the tuba-house. Have you noticed he's left-handed? He stopped behind the fellow, reached up with his right hand for the basket, with his left for the bolo and shoved it in between the blackguard's ribs". "Did he give him no warning?", I asked naively. "Warning? and risk his own life?". Geronimo was increulous that anyone could be so simple-minded, "Stupido! Burro!, that only happens in the cowboy movies" .... Geronimo's yarns put a bad thought in my head. There is a story that long ago a woman in Rome called Joan got herseft passed for a man and ended up pope. She was only discovered in the pangs of childbirth. She and her offspring got short shrift. Or so the story goes. Bernini's baldechino in St. Peter's would lend some credence to it, by all accounts. They say there is a birthing-chair made of porphyry, hidden somewhere in the Vatican to this day. Because of Joan, when each new pope was being installed, he had to sit in the birthing-chair, and the youngest cardinal's job was to reach up through the hole, to make sure he had the where-with-all. Depending on what he discovered, he would chant, 'Habet duo', and the Sistine choir would answer, 'Deo gratias', and all was well, even though the choir-boys' hearts weren't in it, for personal reasons of their own; for they had been tampered with too, as everybody knows. If he sang out, 'Habet unum', the choir would answer, 'Deus sufficit, it'll have to do'. That made the boys in the choir, young and old, a bit less discontented with their lot. But if he chanted, "Habet nullum", in profound silence he was led away to the choir; it made their day. The things that were done in the name of Holy Mother Church, to guard the faith or to reach a high 'C'. If Rosie ever made pope, they would need that chair again. God forgive me, I have a wicked imagination; you should hear the Filipino priests themselves; they dont spare the fancy-pants put over them.

8.6.67 : The priesthood is basically a call to serve the people; it guarantees the grace to do the job. A life of celibacy is totally different, what is called charismatic; it guarantees a totally different grace. The two are as different as chalk and cheese. The thought nags persistantly that Rome drives people like me out unjustly. I am angry because I know I have every right to stay in.

7.7.67 : The bishop, a Tippman and a Philippine citizen, is a kindly soul, though straight-laced and something of a safety-pin. Peter wont start any revolutions but he loves bridge; a great three no-trump man; cant sleep after a game; sees the card in his head that he should have played. Last Sunday night we were playing and Dick was hovering as usual, gawking over shoulders, whispering unsought, unwelcome advice. To get rid of him politely, someone said, "Dick, why dont you make us a limerick on himself there", sticking out his lower lip in the direction of the bishop engrossed in the play. While the next hand was being dealt, the droll Dublin twang came from over by the open window ....

There was a young lady from Chicester
Who's curves made the saints in their niches stir
When she hipped up the aisle she made the folks smile
And even the good bishop in his britches stir.

30.8.67 : The cards were still going strong when the young lads came home from the pictures; they were talking about Marlon Brando in West Side Story. Dick was off and running

There was a young lady called Wooster

Who dreamt Marlon Brando seduced her

She woke up to find it was all in her mind

A lump in the matress had goosed her.

The psychologists call this phenomenon sublimation; if you repress an urge at one level, it breaks out at a higher level, like a valve on a boiler. You're only kicking the problem upstairs. The experts who write the weighty tomes about the celibate priest would do well to delve a little in that fertile field of the clerical joke, clever, witty, outrageous, sophisticated, bitter, funny, misogynous, sad, puerile, drawing the guffaw that speaks volumes, or the snide snigger; our life in a nutshell, laughing and crying and not really sure why. No doubt, God can use any instrument as a vehicle of his grace, even the jaw-bone of an ass, we are told. I wonder is that a sly prophecy fore-telling some of the abysmal sermons we have inflicted on the long-suffering fathful down the years; Anyway, the stark truth is that this cult of enforced celibacy causes many priests to be stunted in their relationships with women and men. How could it be otherwise? A wise old monk once said to me, "Celibacy in itself is neutral, neither good nor bad, a blessing or a curse. I sometimes wonder if enforced celebacy is anything other than a primitive power fetish".

15.9.67 : Billingsgate and Moore Street are famous for colour-ful language. We have a character here by the name of Noll; no fishwife could hold a candle to him. I'm no prude but it's shock-ing to hear filth in the mouth of a priest; he thinks it makes him macho. He can switch it off like a light; as polite as you please in front of the bishop or rich oul wans who might be good for a few bob. Noll was describing how he got home last Monday morning in the wee hours. He swears he was as sober as a judge. Be that as it may, he failed to curve on a curving bridge.

Said bridge is 300 yards long and consists of a two parallel planks up on trestles, about 30 feet above an estuary. The bridge went right and the jeep went straight. As luck would have it, it landed on it's wheels in twenty feet of water. Noll scrambled out and woke up a logger nearby, who got a winch on the jeep and hauled it out in the moonlight. No trouble finding it because the lights were still shining under the water. Uncle Sam built a good jeep. I leave it to yourself to fill in a liberal sprinkling of expletives Noll painted the so-and-so bridge with.

25.10.67 : Most people, even those who think they are atheists, have some idea of God in their heads. Very few think, in the real sense of the word. I am no genius myself, but I can count on the fingers of one hand, those I have met so far, whose brains fire on more than one cylinder, and two of them were women. We priests spent years studying; very few of us can grasp a truth as simple as one and one make two - God is not identical with the idea I have of Him in my head. If He exists, and I think He does, He has to be totally different from every thing. That seems cold comfort but it is my comfort. That is the rock of my life; it hit me like a bolt from the blue one day when I was plodding along in the heat behind the bodyguards. The path was steep; the sweat was in my eyes; the harsh jungle sounds of disturbed birds and monkeys grated in my ears; tall trees soared straight to the shadowed roof, like the pillars of a mighty cathedral; the walls were festooned with hanging painted flowers vivid as a rainbow in twilight. We came to a window in the trees. I stood there staring at the sloping green carpet stretching away to the fringe of bright yellow strand and the blinding blue sea. This was what my eyes were looking at. But I was not there. I was far away, a child again in the bog under a cold lowering sky; a hint of frost tinged the air blue-black against the peat-face; a cock blackbird squawked as he swept along the turf bank and pitched in a silver birch. Exodus calls Him 'He is'. St. John calls Him 'Love'. We mouth our baby sounds; maybe to call Him 'She' would be nearer the mark.

15.12.67 : Thoughts go back home as Christmas draws near. Here we are with the heat and mosquitos; imagine yearning for dark days and cold, wet evenings with a hint of frost. Just got back from a barrio on the shore of Lake Lanao, Muslim country. These children of Allah have some peculiar habits, by any standard; they use the lake for everything, literally. They drink it; they bathe in it; they fish in it; they relieve themselves in it, squatting so that their bodily functions take place under the water. But they are in the majority and not inclined to compromise, so the Christian motto is, 'Dont drink the water'. The transistor radio is everywhere now. I woke up one night to the strains of Danny Boy. The Beatles are here, and Sinatra singing 'Strangers in the Night'. A boy with a guitar brought the tears to my eyes with 'Gotta make a sentimental journey, sentimental journey back home'.

16.1.68 : I'm in my new assignment, a cane-sugar refinery; it's called the Azuchar Central; a sort of one-horse parish all my own. I like it. I'm 38 and standing on my own two feet for the first time. And I'm closer to the way the ordinary people live here. Dont get me wrong; the order does mighty work here; most of them are as poor as church mice in their personal living. But the whole system; the colossal buildings modelled on the monolithic church; the luxuries; the air-conditioning recently introduced; the food and drink; the lifestyle; all more on a par with the hacienderos than with 90% of the people. No one asks the obvious question, 'What in God's name are we doing here anyway?'. I have talked to many young Filipino priests, including some I taught myself. They dont want to go back to the barrios; we have made aristocrats of them as well. Anyway, for better or for worse, I'm on my own now. It's clear that the poor people are getting screwed here; up to their ears in debt to the company. The man before me here started a credit union; a move in the right direction. But saving is totally alien to them; it will take time to break the habit of spending before you earn.

7.2.68 : Dont get me wrong; celibacy can be a good thing, an asset in the church; celibacy for the sake of the kingdom of God has solid roots in scripture. It is enforced celibacy that is the problem. The true history of this law makes for fascinating reading. Ordinary Catholics have been kept in the dark, we were not told that the main reasons for the law at the time were political and economic. Now the church is built on it; the missions as we know them cannot function any other way. Those who have a static view of the church see the whole structure tumbling down, if this law is tampered with. There is not a hope of such radical reform in my lifetime. But it must come one day. The scriptural model par excellence for all Christians is the Incarnation, 'the Word was made flesh', the marriage of Christ with His bride the church. Imagine a married pope; imagine a husband and wife setting out on the missions; imagine a woman running the Vatican. It seems preposterous, only because of our mind-sets. All that it violates is convention, and convention is often a sacred cow, much more important than God's law. Jesus criticised the Pharisees for neglecting the weighty things for their 'traditions of the ancients'.

3.3.68 : I seem to be brooding a great deal these days; morose thoughts. The history of celibacy makes sober reading; reading between the lines, of course. The official history was written, as always, by the winners of the war. For it was a true war, fought, as always, for reasons that seemed good at the time. Like all wars it had casualties and unknown soldiers. From the beginning there were two categories, parish priests and monks. But in the eleventh century there was a war on for control of the world, between the pope and the emperor. Hildebrand was a monk and he became Pope Gregory V11[1073-1085]. His strategy was, centralise the manpower and the finances of the church; make all the priests monks and cut out the simony, the middleman. No more local communities; one monolithic church under an army of shock-troops directly answerable to Rome. Gregory did reform the church and he vanquished the emperor, who came to him on his knees. His main man in this struggle was a monk called St. Peter Damien, a woman-hater if ever there was one; Damien must have had serious problems with his mother growing up; the things he says about women would make your flesh creep; nobody before or since has come near him for vilifying womankind; he had a mind like a sewer. He was fond of calling the wives of priests, who had been married lawfully for as much as forty years, sluts, harlots, common whores, the devil's cloaca, and other such filth too obscene to repeat, even in Latin. Verba piis auribus offensiva was the official term. To put the fear of God in the rest, he forced some priests' wives to be sold into slavery to the Barbery pirates. I suppose Gregory reasoned that you cant make an omelette without breaking eggs. Like so many with good intentions, the end justified the means, not in theory, but in practice. He is all the more to blame for using this pychopath to do the dirtywork. The ultimate irony is that Peter Damien is a canonised saint today; not all the saints were angels; and here I sit in the Catholic Philippines in the year of Our Lord 1968, and try to explain to them why they merit no saint at all, good or bad, in 400 years. Incidentally, one of the reasons why a later pope, Hadrian 1V [1154-1159], who happened also to be an Englishman, wrote a Bull backing the Norman invasion of Ireland, was because the Irish clergy had ignored the law of celibacy; they were too far away for Rome to be able to enforce it. This was the chance to bring the wild Irish into line. I'm as far away from Rome as one can get; how do I know all this? I have been talking to a man who did some rooting around in the Vatican archives in his day. End of history lesson.

14.4.68 : What a wonderful thing it would be to have someone to talk to; to share soul-secrets I have never breathed to a living soul. God knows them of course and that is a comfort. But He made us to need a help-mate; everybody needs a better half; it surely is not good for a man to be alone; He never said a truer word. Now I can see that the best of the priests are so in spite of the regime; those bachelor types who suit this life, while they do great work, in general they dont relate well to people. Of course there are some exceptions who break all the rules. Some say the cream of the crop are leaving; others that the rats

143

are abandoning the sinking ship. In my opinion, the ship needs an overhaul. And I am becoming a crank; I shoulda never left home.

27.4.68 : I helped Fr Roca with the confessions for Holy Week. They came down from the mountains in their thousands. We were at it from morning till night all week, with an odd ten-minute break for a cup of coffee and a few puffs on a tustus. And still never an end in sight. Holy Thursday was the limit. The big stone church and the whole plaza were packed. I said the only thing for it was a general absolution, like troops going into battle, "Many of them will be dead by this time next year; their only chance, and it means so much to them". He went for it, for he had been an army chaplain. It took three hours to give Holy Communion out of gallon sweety jars. The arms were dropping off me by the time we got through. On Good Friday they re-enact the Lord's Passion. A young man volunteers to be Christ. This is not make-believe; it's for real, short of driving in the nails. People follow the Way of the Cross on their knees, usually a mother and father fulfilling a vow made when their child was sick. They love Fr. Roca and kiss his hands. He is a good man, even if he is a bit crazy. He said to me, "I am too old to make a change now, but there is no life lonelier than that of an old priest".

31.5.68 : We have a good choir here; mostly girls in their late teens and seven or eight boys with guitars. They are full of music; they hear a tune a couple of times and can sing it in parts. Carmel is in charge, four-fifths Spanish haciendera, convent-bred, in her mid-thirties, still unmarried. They practise in the priest's house twice a week. Great company. All anxious to improve their English so we talk a mixture. My housekeeper is ancient and no great cook; so I eat wherever I happen to be. With my first pay-check I bought a Zenith radio; on Saturday nights to 2am I listen to the rugby; early start on Sunday mornings; Mass at 6am. The choir has big plans to go round the haciendas next Christmas singing carols. One of the boys, Benny, lost a leg when he was ten; the children climb on the train bringing the sugar-cane in from the fields, and he fell off. The choir is going to buy him a wooden leg for Christmas.

26.6.68 : We had a picnic. Borrowed the company bedford and we all piled in and climbed on and went to the beach for the day. Beside the sea is like paradise lost; shade from the broiling sun under the palm trees; the warm water a deep blue-green ; no mosquitos; dining on lechon, young pig roasted on a spit, and drinking cocoanut milk from the shell, and mangos for dessert. All the girls wear long dresses in the water; the big boys shorts, the small boys nothing only homemade goggles. No danger from sharks inside the reef. Under water in the lagoon is a fantastic world all it's own; coral of every shape; a forest of trees and plants and streamers waving gently in the currents; little flat fish of every hue darting in and out in the under-growth. The little boys have guns made from a piece of wood, a strip of rubber and a knitting-needle. The fish are wise and keep you head on; the trick is to get a side-shot. Wee lads of seven or eight can stay down up to three minutes. I am up to about forty seconds, which is a very long time when your lungs are bursting. When the fish are out of the water they lose their rainbow colours right before your eyes. We played water-polo with a basket-ball. One tall girl in the choir, a teacher of twenty-two, ploughed into me a couple of times. I'm not sure it wasn't an accident on purpose. Jeff, you better watch it; she's easy on the eyes .... When they're all gone at night the craziest schemes make sense. If I could find the right one and if I could make the break, we could go back to Ando. We could survive somehow; Terry could come and stay with us. The people would take us to their hearts. In the grim light of day, it's a very different story. The truth is that I haven't got the guts to break the mould, to defy the conventions. I'm good at making excuses, and blaming the pope, and moaning and lamenting about the failure of the council. The problem is in my own head; I haven't got the courage of my convictions. I have only one life to live and only God to answer to, but I cant face it. Until men like me take the bull by the horns, nothing will change.

145

20.7.68 : I was thinking of that legend of Pope Joan and the mystery of the birthing-chair in the Vatican. The canon law is very particular about pedigree as well as gender in the clergy. Did you know that a male born out of wedlock, vulgarly known as a bastard, cannot become a priest? Whether this had any connection with Joan or not, they used to examine the candidates to make sure they were 'whole', as they say about horses. The practice has been discontinued, at least in our order. One of the old Filipino priests was telling me that the Spaniards were still groping the candidates in his time.

8.8.68 : I went to a fiesta on the motor-bike, which is great for the mountain trails in the dry season. Who was there only the tall teacher? When it was time to go home she asked me for a lift. I was a bit surprised but could hardly refuse. There is always some busybody to carry stories, and they never lose in the telling. We mightn't be seen in the dark. A woman had got that near me only once before. This was playing with fire, but I couldn't resist. So it was with mixed-up feelings of adventure and trepidation, and several other nameless stirrings, that Jeff headed down the mountain with his pillion-rider. To tell the truth he was shaking like a leaf. I must admit it was fun, even the tumble, when the back wheel went out from under her and left her sitting on her bottom laughing. She straddled on again and wrapped her long arms tighter round me, and I did my best to concentrate on the bumpy terrain. But I couldn't help noticing the feel of her long thighs and her breasts like two pears against my back. She hopped off before we reached the lights at the gate, "Muy gratias, padre", and she slipped into the night, leaving me in an utter state of chassis.

3.9.68 : I cant see myself lasting too long here. In my heart I know I will leave the priesthood sooner or later. But I'm not ready yet. I just couldn't do it at present. What worries me is the danger of getting involved first; to me that would be putting the cart before the horse. Maybe I'm cold-blooded but I have no intention of falling in love as they call it, until I'm good and ready. Filipino women are very decent, straight; you know where you stand with them. There is a type of pious Irishwoman, married or single, a menace to a priest; she wants it both ways; all warm and cuddly until he makes a false move; she's horrified and screeches like a stuck pig. Another dangerous type hasn't enough self-respect to avoid getting taken advantage of by the selfish priest. I hear stories; some priests are unbelievably selfish; leave women in the lurch without a qualm. Ah, good Lord, the sins of the fathers and the mothers; what webs we weave. Take the tall teacher here; it is hard for a teacher to get a man; her education scares the bejasus out of the locals. She likes me and I like her. She is dying to get to the States. She is not squeamish. But I know she would never let it get beyond fun and banter, unless she got a sign. It's my own weakness that worries me. So, although I love it here, I'm afraid I wont be staying long. Maybe it's only back in Ireland that I can get myself sorted out.

14.10.68 : By no stretch of the imagination has it been a good year for me. I respect the Pope because of his office; as the man for the job he leaves much to be desired, God help him. He is weak; one has only to compare him to John. Humanae vitae on birth control is excellent as the ideal to aim for: nothing new here; we knew all this already. As a practical guide for married couples living in the real world, which it purports to be, it has all the hallmarks of the celibate living in an ivory tower. In practice, in the individual case, morality is often the choice of the least sinful of a number of evils. No moral decision is ever cut and dried. In my opinion, Paul overstepped his role when he took it away from the council. Second mistake, he threw four years of his own commission's work in the trash-can and now proceeds off his own bat, just like Pius X11. Would John have done this? Definitely not. What is the sound Catholic teaching on this matter? It's not all that complicated. If contraception, of whatever kind, aborts the fertilised egg, even in the very moment of conception, that is murder. If contraception, of whatever kind, artificial or otherwise, merely prevents the sperm from fertilising the ovum, that cannot be proved from

God's law, to be morally wrong. Paul does not prove that; he merely says so. But on what authority? Even the pope cannot make something wrong by merely saying so. He has over-reached himself in imposing this ban as if it were God's law. Is it not arrogant of me to presume to criticise the pope? No. Couples are expected to understand. The priest is the one who makes contact with the human soul in confession; he has to square with his own conscience what he imposes as binding on others ... Women's lib has a good case; women are second-class citizens of church and state. For example, one doesn't have to be a genius to figure out that God's law demands equal pay for equal work They have indeed some head-cases. who spoil their cause, give it a bad name. For instance, instead of demanding abortion as a woman's right, they should be pushing for male contraception; a pill for the men is what I say. Would men take it?

2.11.68 : Filipinos ask me what's going on in holy Ireland, the island of saints and scholars. I try my best to explain this insanity. A bunch of students in Queens, Belfast, with Bernadette Devlin the ringleader, started copying the civil rights campaign of M L King in the States. Here comes this man-of-God Paisley, built like a bull carabao and voice to match, with his gang of red-neck Orange bigots to defend Protestant Ulster with cudgels, and put manners on the papists. And lo, the dead arose; re-enter the IRA to the defence of faith and fatherland. Gerry Fitt is no bargain; Devlin is no sweetheart; Paisley is a poisonous wind-bag; when you have the fearless patriots for friends you dont need enemies. Some motley crew. God help Dev's Ireland. Some here think it's a joke; a storm in a tea-cup; I think we're back to 1912; the hounds are still baying for blood, orange + green = red. As it was from the beginning, is now, and ever shall be, the old men keep on talking; the young men keep on dying; the women and children go on suffering. And what will the churchmen, the defenders of the faith, do?   A hard chaw here was not very reverent, "What they have always done, mouth pious platitudes and cover their arses".

4.12.68 : Remember back in '62 I wanted to say one Mass in the dialect for Christmas; they said I was mad. This year I begged for permission to have one Mass in Latin, the lively one with the dancing and maracas, just for Christmas for old times' sake. The boss refused permission, "Are you mad"?. And only Jeff sees the irony. I'm going ahead anyway. I cant stand stupidity; God Almighty, if Rome told some of them to jump from a height, they'd do it out of holy obedience. Horse manure! Some hypocrites know what they're doing and some dont know any better, God help them .... About the contraception, the sad thing is that the Holy Ghost would have guided us into the truth if Paul had only trusted the church. It is the exaggerated power of the papacy that is at stake here rather than a moral issue. There is no question of me leaving the priesthood over this alone, but how can I in conscience impose this directive on people in confession? I cannot. I can just imagine what answer Christ would give me on the day of judgement if I came up with the excuse, "But, Lord, the pope said it". I have been up against it a couple of times already in confession, but the numbers are falling off drastically these days. Many priests are leaving.

Christmas 68 : An eventful year; Bobby Kennedy and Martin Luther King dead, murdered by fanatics; the ghost of Marilyn haunts the Kennedys; King a Christian martyr. Paul V1's ruling on birth-control the last straw; my own maelstrom, waking and sleeping. I'm hanging on but my heart isn't in it anymore. It's hard to face the spectre of guilt, being thought a traitor; God alone have I to answer to and he will judge me on my conscience. The priesthood is in a straitjacket not of Christ's making; that's the long and the short of it. John hadn't time to put the reform into practice; God's ways surely are strange. The lay people have been wakened but the Vatican clamped down the lid; who can foresee the consequences? Reform has boiled down to pitching out the Latin and the heavenly music and the marble altars bought with the hardearned coppers of the poor. Ah my poor mother; she calls it a Protestant Mass now. What a terrible thought that I'll never say Mass again; like having my heart torn out. It would be much easier to stay in spite of the sting of the flesh. What do I want anyway? I want truth and justice from top to bottom in the church, the whole gospel. Women and children and the poor must be treated fairly. If a clergyman compromises the church we are all tarred with the same brush. A priest or a brother abuses a child and it is hushed up. The bad apples may be few but it only takes one to rot the whole barrel, when they are covered up by privilege. God's people still live in fear. They caught a fleeting glimpse of the beautiful face of Christ for a little while in the jolly face of John, but no more. The blinds is down, Joxer, the blinds is down. Deep, deep down I'm at peace whatever the future brings, but I'm hellish lonely. There's that nice girl here, the tall teacher, it would be easy to get friendly with; I dont dare; I'd have to run again, not for the first time. You know how quick talk could start if I didn't keep my distance .... We need prayers more than God does, or we gradually forget Him; when one finds it hard to pray and God seems far away, a decade of the rosary comes in handy; an old reliable to fall back on.

Chapter 9

12.1.69 : The carol-singing went well. We sang and the hacien-deros' wives sent out a donation for Benny's wooden leg and goodies for us peons. There is a 9-hole golf course here. This is my first chance to play and I'm doing well. Four of us go straight from morning Mass and get nine holes in before break-fast. It's a chance to get to know the big-shots. They all came to Mass for Christmas and I let them have it; didn't put a tooth in it. They're getting a terrific price for sugar now that Cuba's closed. They better start taking better care of their tenants and workers, or the Communists will take over and they'll have to go back to Spain where they came from. We have some fierce arguments at the golf. The decent men among them are under pressure from the scoundrels who treat the people like dirt. And they sure dont like a priest who wont tip his cap to the gentry and who calls their trade union a sick joke. Rumbles already of complaints to my boss about sending them a commie padre. My bet is my days are numbered; our days are numbered in the PI .... A girl arrived home from Manila for Christmas. I bring com-munion to her bed-ridden mother, a lovely lady. She was left a widow when the children were small; she loves to tell me how well they have done. The daughter is a real smasher. She came running into my place out of a downpour, drenched to the skin. I insisted she change into dry things in the bed-room. Off she sailed in Jeff's shirt and baggy trousers, leaving an invitation to come for dinner on New Year's. She was dressed to the nines when I got there; yellow muu muu down to the ground and a flower in her hair. And she is some cook. After a wonderful meal and spending time with her mother, we walked in the gar-den. She wanted my advice, "A GI from Hartford, Connecticut, has asked me to marry him. I cant leave mother all alone". We discussed it. He was leaving soon; she couldn't get a passport to follow him. Would he come back for her? She only saw her mother twice a year as it was. It puzzled me that this girl, about 30, goodlooking and smart, showed no concern for the big question, had he a woman back in the states? Why hadn't she told her mother? There's more here than meets the eye. So I said, "Thelma, what's the score?". She blushed demurely and spilled the beans. He is a GI all right, but a chaplain, a priest. You cant be up to the women. She had no photograph. Was there really a lonely chaplain seeking a soul-mate, or was she fishing? She promises to send me a picture.

22.2.69 : Sometimes when I'm sitting here alone at night, and they're all gone, and there's nothing on the wireless, I fall into a kind of reverie. There is one lesson we learned from the first day in my father's house, the appeal to reason. A thing has to add up. Even the faith is reasonable; it makes sense to believe in God and to take Him at His word. I am indeed a sore-head and a crank, but all the things that are wrong in the church dont sit easy with me. I'm too logical for my own good. I know men are human; I am nobody's judge. However, saying one thing and doing another, only one name for that, hypocrisy. What did Christ mean by, 'He who can take it, let him take it'? What did Paul mean by,'It is better to marry than to burn'? .... Maggy says little Terry is a big girl now; she's nearly nine; very like her mother. I'd love to see her but it's better to let things be; what she doesn't know wont hurt her. She goes to Ando every Christmas; Mrs. Maguirre keeps me informed. She spends most of the summer on Goladuff with my mother. Mother still writes faithfully every month.

4.3.69 : Every month puts a new nail in the coffin. Alas, poor Matty, I knew him well. He did the work of ten. A real man's man. The new word for him would be a workaholic. But more heart than head; vain; he knew his way around, plunging in where angels fear to tread. The kind of man who worked around the clock for weeks, then went out like a light and slept twelve hours straight. Whatever he was about, and knowing the man it would be pretty harmless, he was driving in the city in the wee hours and a girl flagged him down. She had a cock-and-bull story about an emergency; she had to get to an all-night pharmacy for pills for her father, who had a heart condition. Big-hearted, gullible Matty swallowed it, hook, line and sinker, "Hop in, Mary."; every lassy was Mary to Matty. He wasn't concentrating on the driving; the next thing he sees the blue lights of a police-car in his rear-view mirror and panicks..He cut the next corner and landed in the municipal flower-beds. The lady was well-known to the police, who hushed it up to avoid scandal in the church. Close ranks, but at a small price; Matty was on the next plane home. Our gang hadn't one good word for him; no mercy, verbal assassination; all his trojan work was forgot; he had let down the flag; he had sullied the escutheon; he had shit on the eggs. If he had drunk himself to death, no one would have batted an eye. He had consorted with a woman,'unclean, unclean, cover thy nakedness'. Nohow must the natives see the idol's clay feet. We were all called in to headquarters. Out of the whole Irish squad only three of us stood up for him. I asked innocently, did He say, 'cast the first stone' or 'the first to cast a stone'? No doubt, my sarcasm was duly noted one more time. I never was one for the party-line.

23.4.69 : Since this account of my life is for my own eyes only, an aid to my memory, filling a psychological void or whatever, I can say what I like. If other eyes should see and be able to decipher it, they would think me a sex-maniac. Bessy was my first love; we never even touched. I did not know her thoughts, for we never talked of us. If her woman's intuition saw through me, she gave no sign. My heart was hidden under the veil of my piety. Now this many a year she has gone her separate way, and I mine. Her I will never forget; love's young dream .... At the Uni I didn't always keep modesty of the eyes; still I guarded my heart. I scorned the weak and the soft. No female came into my clausura. On a ship I first doubted that the porter at my gate was God-sent. In a cave of giant bats, where dead men's bones guarded the entry, the beauty of woman rushed in on me like a mountain torrent when the south-west wind melts the snow. She laughed a merry laugh for there was nothing to worry about. To this day I cannot think of it, for my love died .... Now I'm pushing 39 and nearing the crossroads. Slowly, painfully I'm learning, 'Physician, heal thyself'. The soul is not an angel; the body is not a devil; woman is not the enemy. The Word was made flesh and pitched His tent among us. What's good enough for Him is good, and surely good enough for me. Woman is His masterpiece; it's all in the bible. Her face is the fairest flower of them all. Her voice is honey from the comb. Her walk is magic. Her hair she wears for a crown. He drew her face, smiling. The heart of the good woman is beyond all price. She marches not to war. I'm learning. Mary His mother is no mamby-pamby but a woman of steel; she stood her ground when the men turned tail and ran for cover. When I get my house in order, the tall teacher and I may make a deal; then again we may not. In the meantime, I have found a friend in her I can talk to, no strings attached. One day I will escape from the woven web, like the bird from the fowlers' snare, ex laquio venantium. That's what He promised, didn't He, "The truth will make you free'. The sins of the fathers are the woof; the sins of the mothers are the warf. The garment He wore was of a piece, woven from the top throughout. He bore our sins on His holy body for a cloak. They hung Him on the tree and cast lots for it, who's it should be. Dont you want to clothe your nakedness in the resurrection garment? Am I going mad?

29.5.69 : It was when it finally dawned on me that it wasn't Christ who was demanding celibacy of me, but Gregory V11 and Peter Damien, that I began to lose the stomach for it. I want to be a priest; I love the work; I get on well with everyone. That side of it is fine. But the sacrifice of human contact; in some cases it may be good, in others, not. Is God asking it of me? I doubt it, says Croker. I am very tired wrestling the angel. I made two lists, the reasons for leaving, the reasons for staying. What will tip the balance? .... You have to be careful here where you put your foot. It gets dark quick; one minute it's bright daylight; the sun drops like a stone and it's as black as a bag when there's no moon. If you stray off the path and step on a cobra, it's lights out. Yesterday I saw a little boy with a baby cobra in a bottle. He feeds him on flies. He started looking up, clapped his two hands together, and there was the stunned fly between his palms. He dropped him in the bottle, dinner for his pet, and stuck the rag back in the neck .... One evening I watched a cat and a snake. Talk about a boxing- match. The snake had a lethal punch, if he could land it; the cat had quick feet and a stiff jab in both paws. An ambidextrous cat defending her kittens; no contest. He stood up; he reared back with his forked tongue quivering; he struck. She sidestepped nimbly and cuffed him up along the side of the head, again and again. Scrambled his brains she did. Calmly she nipped him at the back of the head, ignoring his contortions. The cobra gave up the ghost. The cat walked away, tail high, tip waving like an antenna .... Miss Muu-muu wrote and included a picture. Her priest-friend is real alright; I can understand her reluctance; he is fifty if he is a day, and as bald as an egg. Is she taking the poor fellow for a ride, to book her passage to the US of A?

7.7.69 : It started as harmlessly as a snowball in the Alps. An American company is building a hydro-electric plant here; the wife of the boss Boston Irish. She had a big party for St. Patrick's Day. We were all invited; the booze flowed free; she even had green water in the jacks. She cornered me in the kitchen and started a maudlin rigmarole with neither head nor tail to it, about receiving the sacraments. "I'll come tomorrow and we can talk", I said, and escaped. Cold sober, she told me a sad tale. She had married a Catholic in Boston when she was 18; big splash; but it was a shotgun wedding and he took off inside six weeks and left her high, dry and pregnant. She married her present husband when she was 30; she was now 55; had applied for an annulment; nothing doing, though she knew Cushing well. She had never missed Mass; would she ever be able to go to communion again? I said, "If what you tell me is true, and who am I to doubt it, you can receive communion right now. The shotgun marriage was no marriage". Only one thing I forgot; I didn't ask her to keep her mouth shut, and she has a big mouth. She blabbed. Her name, by the way, is Louise. A Boston priest is very close to them; haunts the place. She told him the good news; he was jealous. He was also stupid, because she had picked me to talk to, precisely because I was not close to the family. No doubt, being ultra-conservative, he also considered me just plain wrong and a menace. He said not a word to me; he marched straight to the bishop and reported me; I'm sure it lost nothing in the telling. So I got hauled on the episcopal carpet. The bishop was not unkind; but he's a bit of an old safety-pin. He conceded that my theology was sound; I hadn't make it up out of whole cloth. But he said, pretty illogically, that the canon law would have to be followed in his diocese, until Rome said otherwise. "But, bishop", I said, "this is a matter of the individual conscience and the internal forum. You yourself admit that this is no new theology. She has a right to communion". He got a bit thick and I did too; "You must go back to that woman and tell her you were wrong". "With all due respect, you will have to tell her yourself; Fr.C could bring the message for you". I did talk to Louise, to tell her she could still receive communion; but for God's sake in any other diocese, to avoid a hassle. I also told her she had a big mouth. But my goose was cooked. Like poor old Matty I got the bum's rush. I'm in Belfast a fortnight and it's bitter cold for July.

1.8.69 : It was a sad parting from the Central; they thought they would see me again in 3 months, but they will never see me again. On the plane I was thinking of the parting of Paul with the people on the seashore at Miletus, as recorded in the Acts of the Apostles, 'When he had finished speaking he knelt down with them all and prayed. By now they were all in tears; they threw their arms around Paul's neck and kissed him; what saddened them most was his saying that they would never see his face again'. I had to be the tough guy and pretend I was coming back, because I couldn't let them touch me. I wanted to have a few minutes alone with the tall teacher, but hadn't the gumption. I just shook her hand the last of all, "I'll write". She was trying to catch my eye; she knew. I couldn't look her in the eye .... Yesterday I was answering a late sick call to the Royal Victoria Hospital, riding along on my bicycle, musing on that first Christmas so long ago; the human bodies hacked with bolos, the blood like on a slaughter-house floor sticking to my shoes, the nurse with the carpenter's ruler, the old fellow taking down the numbers, wetting the stub of a pencil on his tongue, the black pig in the dark. The Black Watch stopped me, here we go again, one more time, "Who?, What?, Where?, Why?'. A car-bomb ripped the night close by; only for the Black Watch I would have been a sight closer; thanks for small mercies .... Got a letter from the tall teacher. She's dying to get to the States to study computers; good money in that and she's smart, but has little hope of ever getting a passport. Could I help? I wrote back and I promised to do all I can. Maybe Imelda might help again, and I thought of my dead Esther. Her Terry is now nine and I'm afraid to face her.

10.9.69 : Imelda is now Mrs. President; methinks it has gone to her head; she chooses to forget her childhood friends of the baclas days. Hobnobs with fawning bishops and cardinals now. Does not approve of priests who put wild ideas in the peasants' heads. The answer is "no". .... I'll have to get out of here, they're lunatics; nothing to choose between Paisley and the IRA; mad dogs. And the churches sit on the fence and mouth pious plati-tudes. Jeff is on the run.

2.12.69 : I was lucky. They sent me up to the glens of Antrim to help out for a fortnight. The old man has a serious drinking problem, so I had to stay on till the young priest came back. The PP has a marvellous library, a wonderful time with the people and the scenery and the books .... The tall teacher is getting des-perate; she hasn't a hope, and she's not getting any younger. I have come up with the craziest notion yet. Since I'm leaving anyway, why dont I do something really worthwhile for some-body who deserves a break?; just take off for the PI and marry her in a regisrty office; I still have residency there. That way I could get her out of the country to Singapore, say. We could shake hands on it and she'd be on her way. Not one word to her, until I can muster up the guts to do it .... In the meantime I'm back here in the mayhem and searching for a way out, like an eel in a basket

16.12.69 : Just got the good word; there's a bishop in the mid-lands who can use me. I took the train to Dublin to see the boss, a classmate, a decent man. "Go ahead, Jeff, if that's what you want", he said, "you're a big boy now", with a twinkle down at me, for he's six-three and built like a beanpole. He pulled out a drawer and handed me a few bob and told me to make my own financial arrangements from now on, "Mum's the word". I need wheels; hope Santy is coming.

8.1.70 : Here I am on the banks of the Shannon. I got an Austin Mini and a tankful of gas for 75 pound from a decent man from Quivvy, and headed south on Little Christmas Day. The snow began to fall silently into the Graine as I came across Aghalane bridge. With a light heart I motored down through Granard, thinking of Carleton trudging for Munster. Big flakes like goose-feathers were still falling quietly on the Bog of Allen away to the left; and I came to the Shannon at Clonmacnois in a white twilight and thought of Joyce. There are four priests here, three of them teaching fulltime. They park their cars in the sta-bles. The Austin mini looks like a wee runt of a shabby pony beside the thoroughbreds. Only one man showed any warmth to the stranger; Maynoothmen are superior types. This tin-lizzie simply wont do at all, already I got a couple of broad hints; the clergy have a status to maintain. I haven't two shekels to rub off one another, so they'll have to put up with this affront to their dignity for awhile. I smile and smile and be a villain; mum's the word and I'm only a humble journeyman and know my place; but they can kiss my grits .... Offaly is a football-mad county; there'll be no holding them if they get out of Leinster.

21.3.70 : I oscillate between leaving and staying like a wag-o-the-wall clock."I will, I won't", In a moment of weaknes in the first heady days of freedom, I made a false move; applied for incardination into the diocese. The reception was frigid. My position would be reviewed at the end of the calendar year, I was curtly informed; no question of permanence; the diocese was very particular. I would be given due notice when my services would no longer be required. At least I know where I stand. As long as it lasts it's out of this world, though my nose has icicles on it every morning in the attic.

24.4.70 : There's a young lassy here of 20 and she's some piece of goods. She helps them to run the parish, so she's in and out at all hours. She's a law unto herself. Without a doubt we have taken a shine to each other, so I better be very careful; she's engaged to a strong farmer and knows on which side the bread is buttered ; I could make a right gomerel of myself. Jimmy and I take turns at locum tenens week about. Several nights I was all alone in the back kitchen, watching the 10 o'clock news and here comes the rat-tat-tat of the high heels on the sidewalk and in the back-door she sweeps, talking a mile a minute, making tea, bustling around, the baby-fat still bouncing on her. There oughta be a law; I could be her father; there's no fool like an old fool .... The austi-mini is gone; it was as good as the job was worth, so I now have wheels that look the part, though she's a crock .... saw Offaly play and was impressed; they'll give it a right rattle soon, with McTague and Cooney and the boys .... They keep throwing money at me here, just because I'm halfway decent, one of themselves, no airs. I dont talk down to them; so the missions taught me something. When I have a little nest-egg saved up, I'm going to ask for two weeks off to attend to personal business. I'm hopping a plane in Shannon and meeting my friend in Manila. Nobody need be one whit the wiser. I told her to sit tight; it wont be long now.

8.6.70 : I just got back from Singapore. It only took a week; we were most businesslike and above board. As far as anybody here knows I was in England. The tall teacher is on her way to tackle the computers; now that she's out of the PI, she can get to the States. Just in time, for Marcos is battening down the hatches. He's getting more like a dictator every day, with Imelda the power behind the throne. .....

10.9.70 : Three families here have made me feel very much at home. I'm always welcome, and if I happen in at mealtime I get a share of whatever's going. One night last week I was free and a couple invited me out. I said we couldn't go into a local pub, there'd be talk, so we went further afield. I thought I was in heaven, up on a bar-stool with a lovely creamy pint. I kept feeling that this was so good, there had to be sin in it somewhere. It hit me that I had missed a big slice of my youth, not the drink so much as the crack. Here I was at forty, hearing real conversation for the first time. The best part of all was when they got to know me enough to relax and forgot I was a priest. Here were my people as I remembered them as a child growing up. It was balm to the soul to be a human being again. It took only two pints and here was I singing "Gugma ko, ngano ba intawon naglimbong ka?", when my turn came.

19.10.70 : There's another family out in the bog along the canal. The son plays for Offaly. The granny rules the roost; no airs and graces there, the salt of the earth. They have me thoroughly spoiled already. A chair is placed in front of the fire, a glass of brandy is put in my hand, "Get that into you; it's a hoor of a day; not a spud dug and it'd freeze the bollocks off a brass monkey". I'm having the time of my life, all the more because I feel it in my bones it's only an interlude; my days are numbered.

12.12.70 : We buried Barney in Clonmacnois. I brought him communion every First Friday and we became friends; some great chats. A soft day like spring and it's nearly Christmas. I sneak away once in a while in the night and sit here amomg the churches in the dark. The dead are very much alive all around me. They are free from the fowlers' net; they dwell in the everywhere and everytime, in the Is; free from the chains of one damn thing after another .... Jesus lambasted the Jews for killing the prophets. The Romans could never stand prophets. Pope John was a prophet; when the gravediggers buried him something died in me; now I know it was my heart. I must soon leave this place and go into exile. The best is yet to come, when we have endured the testing-time.

5.2.71 : It was my turn last Sunday to say Mass for the workers at the power station. It's a pity to see the bog being burned out of a face ; very short-sighted policy; they'll be thumping their craws when it's too late. They told me a good yarn. Mrs. Henshaw is the matriarch of the village. Her grand-daughter works in a pub in town and a farmer, a bit long in the tooth, took a real shine to her. No question of marriage, just randy. Here he comes banging on Mrs. Henshaw's door at three in the morning, drunk as a skunk, looking for the young one. They called the guards; they took their time and your man was still trying to break down the door, roaring like a bull. The oul wan went out a back window, climbed through a hole in the power-station fence, walked past the sleeping night-watchman and phoned the local TD, Oliver. The guards came and took the farmer away to cool off in the clink. The word is that Mrs. Henshaw brought charges against the farmer, and the guards, and the sleeping watchman, and two government ministers. The case was settled out of court and she got a slap of money and the farmer done time.

19.3.71 : Old Paddy and I went to Ballinasloe to see Offaly playing Galway in the league. They have a balanced team. We stopped in Shannon Bridge for two pints. I said they would win the All-Ireland; Paddy is sceptical, too many disappointments down the years .... Sometimes I'm homesick for the Philippines; somehow one was closer to the people there. The people here still put the priest on a pedestal. It's not healthy for priest or people. The Filipinos kiss the priest's hand because he says Mass, but they well know he is a human being like themselves. They dont grovel and put on an act for the priest, what you see is what you get .... So many memories, the women with their long dresses caught up and with their wide hats, wading knee-deep in the flooded fields, planting the young seedlings in the warm water. Placid carabao chewing the cud in the early morning mist, and the white storks stand motionless on stilt legs, or perch on the wide backs.

11.4.71 : The bishop came for confirmation. He is an intellectual and very prim and proper. He's constantly telling the world how all the problems in the north are to be sorted out, as long as he hasn't to hobnob with the Protestant bishops. He was still pontificating at the dinner. The old canon, at the bottom of the table, was tired of the lecturing and wanted a bit o' crack, "Watch me stoppin him in his gallop". He raised his voice; "There was a man called Pat down in Kerry who was fond of the sup". The eyes were still on his lordship but the ears were tuning in to the canon. "He drank the farm and the house fell in, all but one room. He headed for the Fair of Puck. A week later, the PP was strollin up and down in the cool of the evenin, readin his office. He happened to look up; here was Pat comin back from Killorglin, with the puck after him on a bit of a string tied to one horn. Now the PP had lovely shrubs, so he wasn't pleased to see this apparition. He enquired politely where Pat intended housin the billygoat, and was informed that he would have to keep him in the room with him. 'But what about the smell?' his reverence wanted to know. ' Ah God, Father' said Pat, 'he'll have to put up with the smell, the same as meself'". Putting up with boorish oafs was the price of a red hat. The refined face puckered up in distaste and he hastily departed.

5.5.71 : I was up home for a few days. Only two families left on Goladuff, old people and no children. Mother had a stroke and is out of it. It's lonely looking out on the silent lough; no voices now, only the water-fowl calling, back again as it was before the first humans came up the river in their dug-out canoes. The sun sank between the low hills; the shadow-line moved up the trees. Little gusts darted and cut arrows on the water. In my mind's ear came the sounds of youth like yesterday; sports along the shore, and the fiddles and the hob-nails dancing, and the wild laughter, and the creak of oars, and the slap of water against cot sides. All gone; and I still dont know where I'm going.

17.6.71 : I used to hear the old people talking about the stations when I was a child; they always said they should never have been stopped. Imagine my delight to find the stations still going strong here just as they had described them. I arrive and the men are standing around the farmyard in their Sunday best, discussing the weather and the crops. I am ushered into the parlour and installed in an armchair by the fire. The women steal in softly first to confess, then the children; then the men slope in from the yard. Mass around the kitchen table and the oats-money is collected to feed the voracious drooght of the priest's car. Breakfast with the elders follows and the women know their place and dance attendance on their betters. With the venerable man of the house at his right hand, the padre sits in the place of honour, as solemn as a hearse-horse. Threadbare tall tales are raked up of former stations, the curate's magic umbrella and the feeble blessing that couldn't pierce the oul man's hat, and the sly sting in the tail, "Begobs now, they still have the power'. I matched them blow for blow with tales of hurricanes and headhunters. I was tempted to mention the naked women, only that wasn't fit for pious ears in mixed company.

30.7.71 : The tall teacher writes regularly. She made it to San Francisco; she works in a restaurant by day and attends computer classes at night. She has never let a hint drop, nor have I, but I see the day coming when I'll be coming to her for a favour. I think of the Lord's parable of the wily steward planning for the rainy day when he would be thrown out of the stewardship, 'To dig I am not able; to beg I am ashamed'. I sounded out the college here about teaching Greek; I know they need one; the bish turned it down. If I had got a little encouragement I would have lingered on here indefinitely rather than face the music. Maybe it's just as well; I'm almost ready for the high jump. I think I'll try to muster up the courage to write to her and put my cards on the table; sure we're married on paper as it is. Perhaps she wont say no and I'll start coorting her long-distance by epistle.

2.10.71 : Offaly won their first All-Ireland and the whole county went wild. The day after, I heard the rat-tat-tat; was I going to Tullamore to meet the team? Her farmer was in England buying pedigree cattle; would I give her a lift? There's no fool like an old fool. We joined the mad thousands and helped to paint Tullamore. At four am we were sitting out in the bog of Allen, looking at the red moon going down, saying nothing, no need. Maybe it was something she could tell her grandchildren, that she could have had a priest instead of her gentleman farmer but she was too fly. One of these days I'll have to muster up the courage to bare my soul to the tall teacher or I might get myself in real hot water .... Got that letter out today; my hands were shaking. Mindless guilt in the gut is a fearful ghost; I must face him down. I think I'm ready to make the break; just waiting for the postman.

10.11.71 : I was out for a country stroll after lunch and who comes by but the bishop in his big boat of a jalopy with the chauffeur in his peaked cap, and I offered a cheery salute. When I saw the frosty look on the snipe face in the back window, I says to myself, "Oh, oh, what's up? Was it something he ate? If he was a married man I'd say things weren't going too well with him and the missus". The next morning's post brought the answer, as icy as his face; "Reverend Father, may I remind you that the Maynooth statutes lay down that the proper garb for a priest includes the clerical collar and hat. I will ask you, while you are in my diocese, to observe the clerical code. Our people expect it of us, etc, etc. I would also remind you that you are here on sufferance ....". I was flabbergasted; for God's sake, in this day and age, to be minus a collar on a country road in broad daylight. I wondered how he knew what the people expected, when he never mingled with them, or even nodded or smiled from his back seat perch. However, I must eat humble pie; I need the job, for the moment. The dig about being on sufferance rankled but I have to swallow the bitter pill and dashed off a most abject letter soaked in contrition to his lordship. I would be a good boy and would observe the sartorial niceties to the letter in his domain. We had picked up bad habits on the missions; now that I was back in civilisation, I would be most careful not to be a source of scandal to the simple folk. Or words to that effect.

15.5.72 : Life is a funny business. I was helping a farmer with his cattle; a wet morning, mucky gaps and runny cowdung. The annual pilgrimage was going to Lourdes that day. Here comes a phonecall; one of the invalids had left his passport at home. I jumped in the car, broke into the house, found the passport and hit out for Dublin airport. It was going to be touch-and-go. At full gallop I charged in the swing-doors and hit my lord bishop amidships. In full regimentals he was, leading his flock to Lourdes. He was not impressed with my outfit. His nose was visibly affronted at my steamy aroma; essence of cowdung. I think I'll be moving on, even sooner than I had planned. In a way I cant blame his lordship entirely; it must seem barefaced disrespect to him. But there's more to it than that. Like many in authority in the catholic church, he listens to busybodies who run to him with gossip. He and his ilk encourage it; use it as a weapon; a fifth column; the episcopal ears listening in every corner of the diocese. The vigilantes are particularly interested in the young clergy. I know for a fact that I have been reported for loose talk about the community schools, for daring to tell parents that they should have some say in their children's education. The bish sent a lackey to preach all the sermons last Sunday. He quoted me verbatim and condemned it as godless heresy. No doubt his nibs has also heard through the grapevine that a buxom young lassy has been seen frequenting the rectory precincts at ungodly hours; it never loses in the telling. I fear me I'm for the high jump now anyway. The cowdung episode was the last straw. There he was, promenading in all his Santa finery before his worshipping flock, the poor silly sheep under the bondage their feudal baron but still without a shepherd, and this unmannerly, foul-smelling clodhopper barges into his sacred person; maybe even left the smallest wee taste of manure somewhere on the immaculate finery. A few football pals of mine, including the man who's passport I had brought, were over at the bar, mustering up courage to face the horrors of flying for the first time. When I charged in waving the passport, and rocked his lordship back on his haunches and knocked the wind out of him, they raised a ragged cheer. You'd think I had scored the winning point. That didn't help. No doubt we'll have another heart-warming letter as soon as he gets back. No doubt also that his sources have him up to date on a few sick boyos he keeps shifting from pillar to post; they likes boys, and girls, shall we say. That little matter he chooses to sweep under the carpet, despite the Lord's warning about the millstone round his neck. I told the guards what I know for a fact, but of course they know the score and give me that look and sing dumb. Church and State, how are ya? Someday the birds will come home to roost. And I must go upon my way sorrowful.

7.6.72 : The episcopal summons arrived this morning. I am bid to the palace next Thursday at ten o'clock sharp. This is it. I should be shaking in my shoes but I dont give one damn; I'm walking on air; the tall teacher wants me. I wear her lovely letter next my heart like armour-plate, so who's afraid of a bishop? .... These days I brood on what I am needlessly losing. I was thinking of, shall we say, the sexual preferences of Filipino and Irish clergy whom I have known, (despite having come across some bad apples, I am proud of having worked with this great body of men, and am brokenhearted to have to go). A great many of both plough the lone furrow manfully; I should know. But there are many exceptions too. If a Filipino priest is so inclined, he may take unto himself a woman, and continue as a priest, if his bishop lets him; no great hang-ups. If he has a different bent, as is quite common, he finds himself a consenting adult and solves his own conscience. Again, no big deal. In contrast, many Irish priests are fixated on sex, in the mind, repelled and fascinated. We fear it and still are fatally attracted. We cant take it and we cant leave it alone. In the Philippines they take compulsory celibacy with a grain of salt. In Ireland, it is clamped on the soul like an iron band, and erupts either in drunkenness or in awful, callous crimes against innocent children, whose silent cries echo to high heaven for vengeance. Those who sanctimoniously cover up this abomination have the greater guilt. There has to be a Judgment Day.

11.6.72 : I was ushered into the august presence. I remained standing for the very simple reason that I wasn't asked to sit down. His lordship checked his watch, "I can spare exactly five minutes. Your services will no longer be required after December 31st". Calling a bishop 'my lord' stuck in my craw; however, we must be polite at all costs. I said, "My lord, as of today I give one month's notice". We still had four minutes. I thought it would be nice to tell this pompous ass, with his red socks and buckle shoes, a thing or two about the missions. It was tempting to tell him what a Filipino bishop said about his own cousin, a future cardinal, "I know plenty of old women who have more balls than our Rosie"; that wouldn't do. So I waxed satirical instead, "The Filipinos have some peculiar customs. The guest is first invited to sit down. Next he is asked, in their strange idiom, if he has a mouth on him?". Before he could field this haymaker, I asked coyly, "Would there happen to be a cup of cold water about the place?". He looked daggers. God help the poor puppet; he never came across an animal like this before. He has no problem with celibacy; he has no trouble blending piety with ambition; I could see the tight face peering in the mirror every morning, fancying himself in a red hat. So we parted.

15.7.72 : I'm in the Three Jolly Pidgeons on the road to God knows where; not a soul here; the old lady went to bed and left me to fend for myself. They had a farewell party for me; like the wedding-guest in the story, his lordship didn't turn up though he was invited. I didn't expect him, though I had worked for him all these months and hadn't cost him a penny. The people paid me, God bless them; stuffed pound-notes and fivers in every pocket and down my shirt. God help him, he means well. He would be fairly typical of the bishops I have had dealings with, though a cut above average intellectually, but stunted in other aspects of the personality, and a sorry but willing victim of the system. Rome's rule of thumb in picking bishops would seem to be ,'safety first'. In their cups the brethren and sistern here begged me to stay and they would support me. I told them they were all very brave now but when his nibs came with his crozier they would bow the knee to Baal, then run like rabbits. We held an auction and they gave me three prices for my chairs and tables and took up a collection for the knight of the road. It was hard to part with my little boat on the Shannon; I have only been out in her four times in all. It breaks my heart, all the wonderful people I have left behind on the long trail. And keeping it from mother. But for the first time in my life, I have somebody to go to; a woman who wants me for me myself. It is not good for man to be alone, the good book says. Lorna and I can talk of love later. Tomorrow I go on pilgrimage, to walk the eskers one last time, then the Sem and the covered-walk Mutt and Jeff built. After that I'll head for Clifden and cross to the deserted rocks at Bizerte, if I have to swim it. I'll sleep on straw in the stable and listen to the lost sheep out in the mist. Then Shannon airport and fresh fields and pastures new. Just disappear into thin air.

20.8.72 : In the sober light of day I had second thoughts. "Jeff", I says to myself, "you are no angel, God knows; but you have tried to play by the rules. Why not do this the right way too?". So I went to see the boss. No decenter man. He gave me a one year leave of absence to make sure. I wrote to my friend in Frisco explaining I still have a lot of guilt-baggage to unload. As it happens, she has one year to go as well in her computer course. We have both waited long; we can wait another while. She's willing to wait. First step, I made for London and got a carpentry job with John Murphy and Son on the buildings, the Paddies and the Sikhs. Helping out with Masses in Brixton at the week-ends. My tall teacher's name is Lorna. We write every week. We have talked twice on the phone. She tells me the muu-muu girl dropped her bald chaplain like a hot potato inside six months of setting foot in the US, and has found herself a strapping young fellow with a crew cut.

7.9.72 : I post my letters home from our place in Brixton, so mother is none the wiser. Sometimes I'm tempted to jump on a plane. How can I know whether I can make the break, and take the plunge, and live with my guilt and my conscience and my hang-ups, until I try it? Is it fair to Lorna? Some bargain she's getting.

27.10.72 : Fate took a hand again. I was strolling around on a Sunday afternoon in the East End and ran into a bunch of Filipino sailors off a tramp steamer. To them I was a long lost brother; took me to their bosom. We did a little pub crawl. When they left I went too. The Agamemnon does ten knots, eleven in a pinch. We were headed for Brooklyn via Europe; Hamburg's red lights, where the ladies of leisure display their wares in the front windows; Rotterdam once more; Amsterdam; Fleishing, where we sank a cutter in the river in the dark; Oporto, where we crossed a bridge a mile high, tipsy on port wine. The sailors cant get over me speaking Filipino like a native; showed me all the sights and the beauties of nature. I could have had a girl in every port. In Oporto we got into a bit of a jam in a long bar. With the trouble in Cyprus, a row started between a Greek crew and a Turkish crew and the Filipinos got caught in the middle and hadn't a clue and fought both sides. The paddy wagon came and put us all in the black hole. When I explained in my best Spanish that I was the chaplain, believe it or not they believed me and let me out. Finally we faced out into the Atlantic. But a storm came up in the night, blowing hard from the south-west. We tried to skirt it to the north. The Agamemnon ended up limping into Galway Bay of all places, to escape the gale, and I can make that pilgrimage after all. We leave on Hollontide Day.

31.10.72: Here I am back in Clifden on Hallow Eve night, lying on straw among the ghosts. The sheep call from the mist. I'm back where I started. With the help of God I'm not alone for long more .... The jostling ghosts wont let me sleep; troubled they crowd and jabber, angry, crying, laughing ... The ordination-day and the shining faces; Dad was impressed with the solemnity but still proud of his own; the American constitution, the charter of human liberty, was born out of the Presbyterian tradition ... The first Mass; now no Mass no more ever again ... There was the year of the flu epidemic in the Sem; no Christmas plays, so we got up a farce at the last minute. We called it 'Mutt and mutt'. The plot was slim. Mutt human was the main man, doing Hamlet disguised as Pat ; mutt canine was a neighbour's mongrel called Spot that we stole for the show. Spot was dressed up for the part and sported a handle. Jeff was Bottom, wearing a po with ears for an ass's head. The play consisted of quotations from Shakespeare, stitched together in no particular order, lines such as, 'Now might I do it, Pat' and 'Out, damn Spot' and 'Is this a dogger that I see before me, the handle towards my hand' It brought down the house, but Mutt and Jeff had to dine on their knees for a week.

Memories ...Another long-laid ghost arose, from the time I was down on the rubber plantation in Zamboanga. The morning I was leaving, I was packing up my things in the empty bunk-house when a beautiful girl walked in with a bundle of clothes; her mother had done a wash for me. The girl offered to help me with the packing. "Bueno inday, muy gratias", I said, and we worked away side by side, gathering up my bits and pieces, chatting about this and that. When all was done, I thanked her again and we shook hands. I longed to kiss her but the chains were too strong. Suddenly, on impulse, she threw her arms around me, gave me a big hug and a kiss and was gone. To say she left me in a state of chassis is putting it mildly; it still haunts my dreams.

Memories.... 'There is a tide in the affairs of men'. In my mind I have taken this step a thousand times. This time there is no turning back. That it should come to this. No Mass no more, no mas amor, a terrible choice. Who is such a sailor that he knows all the currents in the tide? ... Pope John was a prophet. The message he brought was that God wants his people to reach full maturity of conscience. The gravediggers buried his prophecy with him. I should never have left home. Hubris the Greeks called it. Oh God be merciful to me, a sinner; but I swear by all that's holy, it is not the hand of the God who slept on Mary's breast, that holds this cruel, bitter cup to my lips.

Memories .... The old Filipino priest quoted Christ, "Think you, when the Son of Man returns, will He find faith upon the earth?. Very few have real faith. Of all the people I have known in a long lifetime, I could count the men and women of real faith on the fingers of one hand The rest never outgrew the childish faith they learned at their mother's knee. Most people's lives are ruled, not by faith but by convention, what the neighbours might think, the latest fad, the price of eggs. They follow the herd, not the heart. God is good; He invites all to the wedding; very few take him up on it; only the humble find the narrow gate".

This old man was one of the few Filipino priests I met who was a real celibate, a true monk. He said, "Celibacy is a gift of God to those He chooses, for a sign to the others, to lift up their hearts. Celibacy as a law imposed is a man-made convention. A square peg in a round hole is an insult to God". He also said,"Man is a bubble floating between nothing and infinity"; "Man is the only animal that loves sport; his favourite pastime is killing his own kind. War is the great human invention and convention; glorified and romanticised. Men deal in death; only God gives life".

Memories .... A boy-soldier dying in Vietnam; he made his confession in Irish. A boy-soldier dying on the Falls; he was black and spoke cockney.

Memories, memories .... Joe was a bachelor we had on Goladuff, who lived in a wee house on the lough shore. He was a magpie for collectables. The upper and lower rooms were loaded to the gunwales; he was confined in the kitchen. Joe's bed was like a boat marooned in a sea of old coats and newspapers. Stray bits of hay-rope and hairy-ned floated on the surface. Here the handle of a turf-barrow was sticking up, there a bicycle-wheel. Near the bed was a wireless, not for listening to but for sitting on .... Joe had an army of cats who were so well-fed that they couldn't be bothered disturbing the mice who inhabited the undergrowth. Never mind the wee frogs who moved in for the winter. They went to sleep till Patrick's Day. It was the mice was the trouble; they kept him awake, rustling around, chewing the newspapers .... "I'll have to get me a mousetrap", Joe said to the neighbour sitting on the wireless. "But Joe", the neighbour said, "how are the mice going to find the trap?".

Memories .... Then there was the time I was down in a place called Negros, where they grow the sweet cane. I caught a heavy cold. The woman of the house where I was staying took me in hand and put me to bed - a mat on the floor. She plied me with a drink with a rummy kick in it - not all the cane went into sugar. It brought me back to a similar concoction laced with poteen we had on Goladuff we called Bessy's droosel.. The sweat came out on me like a pig in a galvanised crow. Then she sent her daughter for the masseur. I wasn't that keen on getting thumped and pummeled and rubbed by some muscleman. Here comes this jolly, buxom matron of about thirty. She proceeded to give me the treatment; her firm fingers working me up and down, back and front. She chattered away to the bana-tee, most politely ignoring the telltale signs of the effect she was having on more than my cold. Her ministrations lulled me to sleep. When I awoke, even the crickets were still. All around me lay sleeping bodies. The cold was gone.

I still cant sleep; just lie here brooding. Our whole life-view and religion is based on the fatal, gratuitous presumption that we started off fully human, that we fell from grace. The fact is that we didn't come down; we are struggling up; we are slowly and painfully becoming human, and we still have a long way to go. That is our destiny, our aim. Any chance we get we revert to the animal in us. Scratch the most sophisticated of us and you have an ape with a memory; the veneer is only skin-deep. Put any man in a mob and he'll soon show his true colours. As the Man said, the gate is narrow, and few there are who find it

....Black thoughts, damnation yawning like a maw; to lose my vocation, lose my soul, fly in the Face of God; all the dread warnings circle in, beating like harpies' wings; defrocked clergyman; spoiled priest. Naked faith brings cold comfort; throwing security, comfort, prestige, social status, my very soul, to the winds; facing out into the bleak, cold world to plow the lone furrow; haunted in this world, damned in the next; no man that puts his hand to the plow and looks back will see the Face of God. God of love, where are you now? They'll say it's the price of him; he'll never have a day's luck. Why does Shakespeare's dart come back to goad me now, "The stroke of death is as a lover's pinch, which hurts and is desired". Woman is man's downfall,we were warned, since the day Eve gave Adam the apple.Yet it says in the same breath that it is not good for man to be alone. We live a little span; why such beauty and such heartache, all for what? .... In the small hours brave conscience rose up and said, "He holds you in the hollow of His Hand", and chased off the circling vultures, and blessed peace stole in, and I fell asleep.

Who can make sense of life? I stand at the crossroads facing God knows what. God, are you there? What are you about? Why do you bother with us, let alone love us? How can the poor souls see His beautiful face when it is veiled by His friends? How can they see the candle when it is covered by a bushel-basket? God, help us; help your poor lost sheep. No wonder they run after every cowboy that goes the road. Goodbye, good Pope John; it didn't take the horse-knackers and the hucksters long to bury you.

Who said man is a bubble floating between nothing and infinity? I think it was Paschal. Boils down to God or zilch; not much choice, denial ot faith; take your pick. It's only a brief candle anyway; here goes. Is there anybody up there? Is it all an illusion? Might as well be hung for the sheep as for the lamb; Lorna, here I come ...

Chapter 10
Epilogue

"Sus", the Filipinos say; it is their version of "Jasus". Sus, that was some saga, the heartache, the sardonic humour, the heady hopes of the halcyon days, the bitter disillusion, the death of the dream. Once I got the hang of the lingo I couldn't put it down. It left me with some answers, and more questions. Here was a soul laid bare. He wrestled long with guilt and finally followed his heart. On this roller-coaster ride I was many things by turns, flabbergasted, drained, exhilarated, sad, and still to a degree groping in the dark. One thing has grown with the story, the confirmation that Esther was indeed my mother. In a very real sense I was born in the reading of it; it took a nobody and made a normal human being of me. I had a mother. What's more, she was good, the special friend of Uncle Father James. I felt a warm glow in my vitals, filling the black hole. For the first time I looked out on the world in wonder and delight.

But what about the missing piece? Who was my father? Fr. James must have had some idea, surely; he was Maggy's brother. Why does he never once mention it? That is the mystery, the blanket silence of the journal on that crucial point; what it does not say jumps out at you. At the same time, it definitely points to Raul as the villain of the piece. That must be it; I could see it all now. The Maguirres had wronged his father. This was sweet revenge, to get a Maguirre in his cluthes, and a virgin at that, and a priest's daughter into the bargain. As an illegal alien, he had her at his mercy; one word and she would have been on the first plane home. He had forced himself on her and she was helpless. As so often, I am the daughter of a brutal man's attack on a helpless woman. I only hope I took after her.

Then I thought of my faithful Tommy, waiting patiently for me all these years. Soon I can go to him with open arms. But first there is some unfinished business to be sorted out. I want to know all. Why does the journal reveal not one word? I was born in no.7; Esther died; Maggy covered it up and took me because she was childless. But she then got pregnant right off and never warmed to me. Father James had to know the whole story. Why is he ignoring it totally, as if it never happened? Mrs. Maguirre must have smelled a rat. I think I have it; Maggy told it to him in confession. The seal of confession prevented him from breathing a word, even a hint in his own secret journal. That code he could not break, even to save his life. That's it; that's why he never came back, avoided me like the plague all these years. After all that had gone before, I thought I had at last found a friend I could trust, that magic week of summer that ended so abruptly. His lips were sealed, but the journal shows that Esther and I were never far from his thoughts. The thing is to find him and get the whole sory.

Did he and Lorna marry? Where is he now? How do I go about this? If he is still a priest, will he tell me the whole truth? If he is not a priest anymore, will he tell me? Has he a family? How about finding that tall, thin man, the confidant of Mutt and Jeff in the old days, and his boss towards the end?

The first leg of the journey was a short one; I found the thin man in Galway. He was kindness itself. When I told him I was Fr. James's niece, he couldn't do enough for me; brought me into the refectory for tea. How times had changed. Fr. James had dropped out of sight, he said, in late 1972. "A few months later he contacted me about his dispensation, but returned the papers untouched, saying he couldn't stomach some of the questions. That was him. We heard through the grapevine that he married and settled in California". As I watched the ascetic face, I could see him and Mutt and Jeff swimming in the buff off Inishboffin.

The next stop was Goladuff, without much hope of any clue there. Only old Robby was left there now, the only soul left on the island, and one leaky cot left from the fleet of yesteryear. All he got from Fr. James was a card at Christmas with no address. The lough was lonely now; after all the crack, never a human voice to be heard over the water, or the slap of the wavelets against the laggin boards; only the wildfowl calling in the lonesome night. Robby never had much to say. I sat again on the little mountain where we ate the boxty and looked out over the eternal sheet of water framed in the sentinel trees. Next stop Ando.

Tia Maria is ageless. She and Mrs. Maguirre and I had a lot of catching-up to do. They were polite as always, but somewhat stiff at first; on their guard, I could sense. When they heard my story they thawed visibly. Uncle Father James had sworn them to secrecy to protect Maggy and to save me from heart-ache, "What she doesn't know wont trouble her". It was Mrs. Maguirre who had paid for my holidays; "Then Padre Jaime disappeared and you never came back. I finally found out that Maggy was dead and Raul was using the money meant for you". They had always suspected Raul of taking advantage of Esther. Fr. James had never said a word, one way or the other, but he must have guessed all along who the culprit was. Yes, he was married, to a Filipina; they too got their cards for Christmas. They were surprised and hurt that he had not kept in touch; he was like one of the family .... Now the seal of confession explained all. Of course, that was it; they had never thought of that. Then we did some crying, passing round the black-and-white picture of Esther in the white dress. Despite the red hair and green eyes, I was plainly my mother's daughter . When I got a chance, I stole away alone to the cave.

From my reading about oriental burial customs I gather that the green jars are not Chinese but Korean. Some of the oldest ones and the broken fragments could go back a thousand years. The one that contains Esther's bones has a mango tree on it. I leaned my cheek against the cool porcelain and hummed, "Gugma ko, ngano ba intawon naglimbong ka? Mama mia, now I know why"

Next stop California. Before I go to Tommy I want the whole story from Uncle James's own lips. When I find him, will he still feel tongue-tied by the seal? When I tell him that I know that Esther was my mother, will he love me for her sake? When he sees how much I know and that I suspect Raul, surely I will see the truth in his face, no matter how he tries to hide it. I just want to be sure. CNN put it on the wire for me, "Girl wishes to find uncle", giving names and details. Someone was bound to hear it and tell him.

The phone wrang. It was he. Still has the soft Fermanagh lilt. He sounded remote; was the seal going to be a problem? He would meet me at the airport .... Even without the card that said TERRY, I would have recognised him. With the fair hair greying only slightly at the temples, he looked young for his years, but the spark was gone. He concentrated on the traffic on the freeway. He avoided my eyes ....

Uncle James is quiet. He and Lorna have a boy and a girl, aged nine and seven. Lorna is a lady; made me right at home, 'mi casa es tua'. She took the children off to the park to give us time together. I came straight to the point, "I know Esther was my mother. Is Raul my father?". He just sat there. I ran upstairs and brought down the journal. He was standing. At the sight of the old brown and green and blue copy-books, his face went white. He began to tremble and he leaned on the chair-back for support. Great heaving sobs welled up, convulsing his whole body. Anguished groans bespoke a soul in torment. I was baffled. The storm raged on and I stood there helpless. When it finally subsided he collapsed into the chair, utterly spent. His voice came faintly, as from far away, "All these years I have been running, hiding, lying to myself. I knew it but my head would not admit what my heart knew all along. I tried to bury it but the ghost haunted me day and night. I convinced myself that it could not have happened, but my heart told me the truth. I would not listen. Thank God, it is over at last. Raul is not your father .... I am".

It was my turn to be stunned. Something can be so obvious that it is invisible. It had been staring me in the face all along and I could not see it. As plain as the nose on your face, they used to say in Shakespeare's time. We two sat there, looking into each other's eyes, so suddenly father and daughter. It will take time to sink in. At such a thunderclap words die on one's lips. He had escaped from his snare and I from mine.

It is extremely delicate. He is touchy, vague on details. I am getting the story in bits and pieces, of how I came to be. He had been most careful; he and Esther had never talked intimately, or touched; no kissing or hanky-panky of any kind. But he was crazy about her: "From the very first time I saw her, I was a goner. She ravished my heart". No word or sign, least of all to her, betrayed what was bottled up inside. Looking back now, he had been hopelssly naive; no doubt her woman's heart had picked up the vibes. Although he was ultra-cautious and kept his distance, the thought of her came to him at all hours, at Mass, in his prayers, saying the office, preaching a sermon, anointing the dying, in his dreams.

It started harmlessly the day he and Esther had gone to the cave, with bowls of rice as offerings to the dead. One thing led to another. They had gone on into the cave, stealing quietly past the sleeping bats, on and on, scrambling over loose rocks, bumping into each other, laughing like excited children. They could feel fresh air fanning their faces. On and on they ventured, until faint light showed ahead and they could see each other faintly, and they came to a beautiful blue-green lagoon deep under the island. Had Esther known about it all the time? The light seemed to be coming up out of the water. They took off their clothes and swam in the warm water like dolphins. The sea was coming and going through an opening under the water. In the daytime the walls were a mauve tint; in the night indigo. They romped and splashed and wrestled like children. They lay side by side and slept in each other's arms. "The last time when I woke the sea was at the ebb and I could see the horizon. Mirrored in the water Venus was setting. It was heaven. It was hell. Esther left for Toronto the next day. I never saw her again". Who am I to judge them; a short love they had, steep was the price.

This new-found joy takes some getting used to; the load has been lifted at last; my heart is singing for the first time. By accident I have struck the shackles from my own father's soul, into the bargain.

In the days after Esther left, he had been sick with anxiety, not about what they had done, but about the possible consequences, the scandal, the disgrace. Like waiting for the big shaker after the first tremors make the house creak, and the lamps sway, and the clock stop. In time, what with wishful thinking, and the memory of her carefree laugh, he gradually convinced himself that all was well, even, unbelievable as that might appear, that nothing at all had happened between them. He had imagined the whole thing. When she died he was heartbroken, but immensely relieved too, until he found out about me and the reign of terror swept over him again like the tide. He lived in constant dread. But again nothing happened. He persuaded himself that the less I knew the better, that he was protecting Maggy, and let himself off the hook again. It was not a proud record; about par for the course; few are men enough to face the music. The experts would call it the classic moral block of the human condition, the primordial sin that flesh is heir to; when conscience calls, duck. "It's so easy to have moral courage, if only one lets go of fear", he mused with a sad smile; "I tried to do it my way"

He was looking forward to bringing me over to Connemara. During the night he woke in a lather of sweat, his pulse racing, in a state of terrible foreboding of impending doom. He was about to open Pandora's box. He knew what was inside, and he didn't want to know. As so often before, he ran, and he kept running. Fear and guilt made a coward of him. He had sneered at the Jansenist brainwashing of the system; inspite of himself he had not escaped it's poison. He hadn't the backbone of a jellyfish, when it came to the crunch. He could recognise denial a mile away in others; he himself had been living half a lifetime of denial.

We have begun the painful yet pleasant process of ironing out the kinks and wrinkles. Old ways die hard. It's going to take time.

He is still full of the church, the love and obsession of his life. He hasn't given up one iota, though he is skeptical; no chip on his shoulder that I can see. As sardonic as ever .... Rome rejected John's reform to save their own jobs. Career men with a veneer of piety; whited sepulchres; the vast majority of the clergy are decent men, but they lack the moral courage of their convictions to challenge the curia. He thinks the church will lose all material possessions and become as poor as Christ. Rome will be brought to it's knees. The whole monolithic edifice will crumble. There will be married priests, and single, and women priests; the concept of priesthood will evolve to meet the needs of the people. There will yet be a second spring; the church will once more seek the pearl of great price, truth will show the Face of God to the people; we will cease claiming to have all answers, and even God Himself in a box ....Women are the great threat to Rome; if they get in, it's bye-bye to the cushy clerical state. He is critical of this pope and he smiles, ... "I feel like the Irish monk Columbanus who wrote to the pope of his time, telling him he wasn't the man for the job and should resign; He slammed the doors and windows on John's reforms and split the church. I better not get on that hobby-horse", he catches himself and laughs. Almost to himself he quotes Christ, "Think you, when the Son of Man returns, will He find faith upon the earth? It's time the weemen got their turn"

When Lorna came back with the children, she straightway picked up the vibes; something was up; perhaps she had put two and two together before any of us. A wise woman. James is a lucky man to have found her.

I became aware of two pairs of staring eyes, one pair brown, the other green. Reflected in them I see myself, single-minded and self-centred. Suddenly I have a sister and a brother and they have names, Lorna and James. The caterpillar is emerging from the lonely cuccoon at last, to smell the roses. If I have a daughter guess what I'll call her?. It takes some getting used to; the nobody all of a sudden has an instant family. Esther can rest in peace. Father and daughter have a lifetime of catching-up to do. God has been true to the word He gave a little girl in a cold attic long ago. I have escaped from the fowler's snare and can spread my wings at last and trust the air. What a joy it is to be somebody.

And to crown all, Tommy is flying in from Toronto tonight. He's coming for his cold-fish. I'll show him. I can see his face when he hears the whole story. I had some slack to take up in the loving-stakes, a body special of my very own to care for, and to care for me. Joy is as hard to take as sorrow, when you're not used to it; but I'm learning fast.

And so, after the beginning and the middle, I have come to the end, which is also another beginning. But that's another story.

The End